Robert V. Fleisig
McMaster University

Guide to Solid Edge® V18

PEARSON

Prentice
Hall

Toronto

Library and Archives Canada Cataloguing in Publication

Fleisig, Robert V., 1970–
    Guide to Solid Edge® V18/Robert V. Fleisig.

ISBN-10: 0-13-196745-2
ISBN-13: 978-0-13-196745-8

1. Engineering design—Data processing. 2. Machine design—Data processing.
3. Engineering models—Data processing. 4. Computer-aided design. I. Title.

TA174.F54 2007   620'.00420285536   C2006-903139-8

ISBN-10: 0-13-196745-2
ISBN-13: 978-0-13-196745-8

Editor-in-Chief: Gary Bennett
Marketing Manager: Michelle Bish
Developmental Editor: Rema Celio
Production Editor: Laura Neves
Copy Editor: Marg Bukta
Production Coordinator: Christine Kwan
Page Layout: Robert V. Fleisig
Art Director: Julia Hall
Cover Design: Anthony Leung
Cover Image: Masterfile

2 3 4 5   11 10 09 08 07

Printed and bound in Canada.

Dedicated to Barbara J. Fleisig

Contents

CHAPTER 1

Introduction

The goal of this manual is to help you learn how to use **computer-aided design (CAD)** software tools to design mechanical parts. At the same time, you will learn to read detail and assembly drawings as well as to improve your visualization skills.

You will learn to use the CAD software tool Solid Edge, which is a mid-range software package in everyday use in industry. You will learn basic concepts and skills that will be easily transferrable to other similar solid modelling CAD software tools such as CATIA, Inventor, NX, Pro/E, SolidWorks, etc. After completing this manual, you will be able to do the following using Solid Edge:

1. Model rigid mechanical parts.
2. Model assemblies composed of rigid mechanical parts.
3. Create complete and correct detail drawings from part models.
4. Create complete and correct assembly drawings from assembly models.

1.1 This Manual

The chapters of this manual will help you learn Solid Edge systematically. Each chapter builds on the knowledge of previous chapters. In most chapters you are asked to follow along in Solid Edge as you read. These instructions are separated from the text of the manual by the use of boxed numbers, shown below.

1 Read this manual.
2 Follow the examples.

To further aid reading, when key terms are introduced they are typeset in **bold**. Any text you are instructed to type is typeset in *italics*. When onscreen elements such as pull-down menu items are referenced, such as *File→New*, and icons, for example, *Select Tool* Select.., these are also printed in *italics*.

Most exercises, found at the ends of chapters, are only available over the internet from www.pearsoned.ca/text/fleisig.

1.2 Solid Modelling

Solid Edge allows you to create, modify, render, and analyze **solid models**. Solid models are mathematically rigorous computer-based representations of arbitrary volumes. A simple example of a solid model is $x^2 + y^2 + z^2 \leq r^2$; that is, a sphere at the origin with radius r. This equation clearly identifies all points in space as either inside or outside the solid. This is the primary function of a solid model. Other examples of **primitives** — simple solid models described by a single equation — are planes, cylinders, and cones.

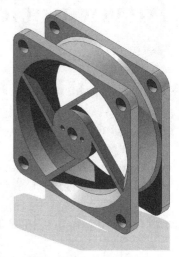

Fig. 1.1

To model complex parts such as the fan housing in Fig. 1.1 primitives alone will not suffice. Instead, a more general solid modelling scheme is employed: **Boundary-representation (B-rep)**. The B-rep scheme rests on the premise that all objects can be modelled from **faces**, **edges**, and **vertices** stitched together to form a closed boundary that separates inside from outside. Examples of B-rep models are shown in Fig. 1.2. In the illustrations of each of the four primitives — cube (Fig. 1.2(a)), cylinder (Fig. 1.2(b)), cone (Fig. 1.2(c)), and sphere (Fig. 1.2(d)) — the faces are shades of grey, the edges are shown in black, and the vertices are denoted by small black circles with a white centre. Notice that not all faces, edges, and vertices are visible and some are only partially visible, such as the edge of the cone. Typically, faces are planar (Fig. 1.2(a)), cylindrical (Fig. 1.2(b)), conical (Fig. 1.2(c)), or spherical (Fig. 1.2(d)). Different types of faces can be combined in a solid model; for example the planar and conical faces of the cone. Edges separate faces. Edges are either separated by vertices as in the cube or are **closed** as in the cylinder. Typically, edges are linear (Fig. 1.2(a)), circular (Fig. 1.2(b)), or elliptical. All kinds of simple and complex shapes can be formed by stitching together faces, edges, and vertices; an example is the fan housing in Fig. 1.1. However, more complex edge and face geometries are sometimes required. These are beyond the scope of this manual.

The vertex, edge, and face elements of the solid model are commonly known as the **geometry**. The other component of a solid model is the **topology**, which defines the

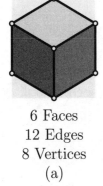

6 Faces	3 Faces	2 Faces	1 Face
12 Edges	2 Edges	1 Edge	No Edges
8 Vertices	No Vertices	1 Vertex	No Vertices
(a)	(b)	(c)	(d)

Fig. 1.2

connectivity of the vertices, edges, and faces. A computer cannot visualize a set of vertices, edges, and faces in space; their arrangement and adjacency information therefore must be stored. The B-rep solid modelling scheme is the engine of Solid Edge and is the de facto standard for virtually all solid modelling software currently on the market.

To the designer, solid modelling is a powerful tool because of what you can do with a solid model. A few applications include the rendering of photorealistic images, simulation of manufacturing operations, kinematic and dynamic analysis, and working drawing generation.

This is in sharp contrast to traditional **computer-aided drafting** software tools such as AutoCAD, which allows its user to draw on the computer. AutoCAD is effective at sharing, reproducing, and modifying engineering drawings. It does not store a model of the design. Solid modelling technology allows users to accomplish these tasks and, in addition, continue the design process with a whole host of applications. In essence, AutoCAD is used for drafting whereas Solid Edge is for designing. As future engineers, you are being trained to design.

1.3   Solid Edge Environments

This manual is divided into three parts covering the **part**, **assembly**, and **draft environments** of Solid Edge. Each chapter begins with a brief list of learning objectives. Use these to validate your progress. The problems will increase in difficulty, with respect to software capabilities and geometry visualization, as the chapters progress.

1.3.1   Part Environment

A Solid Edge part contains a single solid model representing a real-world part plus additional information such as its material. In the Solid Edge part environment, you will learn to create a part, modify it, and manipulate views of the part. Examples of four different parts, representing pieces of a toy, are shown in Fig. 1.3.

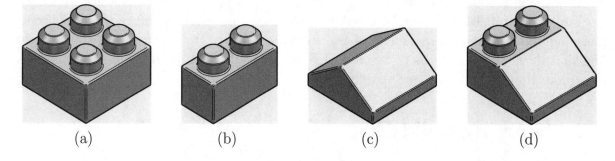

| (a) | (b) | (c) | (d) |

Fig. 1.3

1.3.2 Assembly Environment

A Solid Edge assembly is an arrangement of two or more parts. In the Solid Edge assembly environment, you will learn how to create an assembly, connecting the parts in space using assembly relationships. In addition, you will learn how to create exploded configurations of the assemblies. An assembly of the parts shown in Fig. 1.3 is illustrated in Fig. 1.4.

Fig. 1.4

1.3.3 Draft Environment

In the draft environment, you will learn to produce detail and assembly drawings from parts and assemblies. You will apply dimensions so that assemblies and parts can be fabricated directly from your drawings. A partial detail drawing of the part in Fig. 1.3(d) is shown in Fig. 1.5(a). The partial assembly drawing in Fig. 1.5(b) illustrates how the assembly in Fig. 1.4 was assembled from the parts in Fig. 1.3.

Solid Edge has more than the three environments listed above, but to meet the objectives listed at the beginning of the chapter you will only have to be familiar with the part, assembly, and draft environments. This manual is not intended to provide an exhaustive tutorial on all the capabilities of Solid Edge or any other solid modelling software. However, once you have worked through this manual you will have a strong understanding of the basic concepts. Learning the additional capabilities of the software will be straightforward. You will also find that there are many ways to accomplish a given task in Solid Edge. You are encouraged to explore these capabilities and to experiment.

1.4 Starting Solid Edge

It is assumed that you are familiar with the Windows operating system environment and that Solid Edge is installed and operational. If you are setting up Solid Edge, ensure that

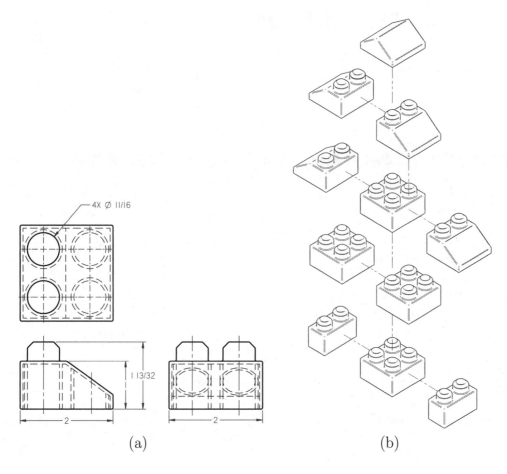

(a)   (b)

Fig. 1.5

all the template files are installed.

All screen shots were taken on Windows XP. Their appearance on Windows 2000 will be different. The difference is only superficial and everything that follows applies. It is recommended that you use a display with a minimum resolution of 1280 pixels × 1024 pixels.

The Solid Edge program handles several types of environments. Each environment allows you to modify a different kind of document. For the purposes of this manual, only the part, assembly, and draft environments are of interest.

Now start Solid Edge. Note that, depending on the installation on your computer, Solid Edge may be located on a different menu. The instructions below reflect the default installation options.

1 In Windows Explorer, click on the Start menu, labelled *Start*.

2 Find the menu *Solid Edge V18*.

The menu will look like Fig. 1.6.

3 Click on *Solid Edge* in this menu.

After a short time your display should appear like Fig. 1.7. It is assumed throughout this manual that *Apprentice Mode* is turned on, as shown in Fig. 1.7.

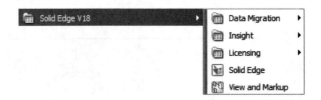

Fig. 1.6

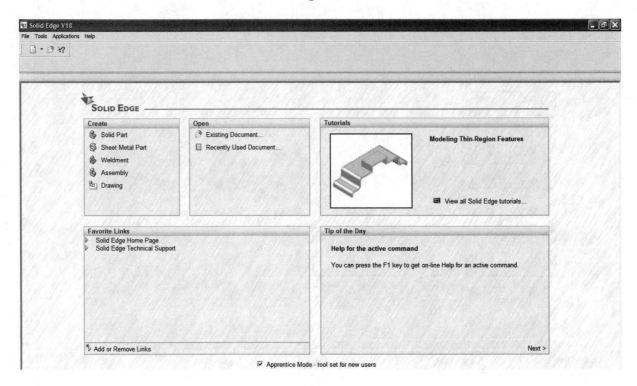

Fig. 1.7

Never start more than one copy of Solid Edge. You can tell if you have more than one running by looking at the Windows taskbar. If more than one Solid Edge application shows up you should close all but one copy of Solid Edge. If you need to open more than one Solid Edge document at a time, open them all from the same copy of Solid Edge.

1.5   Using Help and Tutorials

You will find that many commands are beyond the scope of this manual. When you need additional help you should turn to the online help facilities built into Solid Edge. Help is available on the menu bar (Fig. 1.8), as an icon ⋏? on the main toolbar, and by pressing the *F1* key at any time.

Additionally, on the help menu you will find *Tutorials*. Selecting this item will display the dialogue box shown in Fig. 1.9. As a supplement to this manual you may find the following tutorials useful:

- Part Tutorials

  - Introduction to Part Modeling
  - Modeling Pattern Features in Solid Edge
  - Modeling Parts With Sketches

- Assembly Tutorials

  - Building a Slider Assembly in Solid Edge

- Draft Tutorials

  - Detail Drawings with Solid Edge Draft
  - Producing an Exploded Assembly View

Fig. 1.8

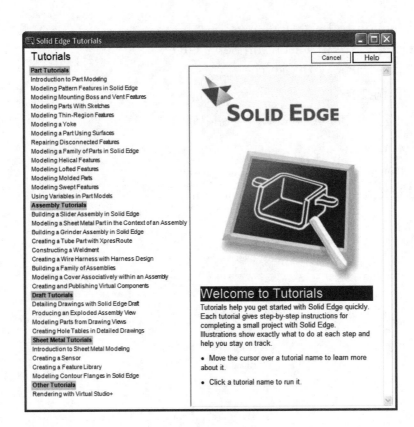

Fig. 1.9

PART I

PART MODELLING

CHAPTER 2

Part Environment

Learning Objectives

After completing this chapter, you will be able to:

1. Create a new part document.
2. Select a part template.
3. Open and save part documents.
4. Set the save reminder.
5. Paint parts.
6. Change the viewpoint of a part.
7. Modify the display of a part.
8. Create and apply 3D view styles to a part.
9. Save a rendered image of a part.
10. Inspect the physical properties of a part.
11. Take measurements of a part.

In this chapter, you will learn the very basics of using the Solid Edge software. First, you will be shown how to create a new part document and perform basic file operations on it. Then, using a sample part document, you will change the view of the part, paint it, save a bitmap of it, and inspect it. These basic functions will be invaluable when learning and using the feature creation and modification capabilities of Solid Edge.

At the end of this chapter exercises will test your knowledge of the learned material.

2.1 Templates

By default when you start Solid Edge, no document will be open. To enter the part environment you must create a new part document either by clicking *File→New* on the menu bar or clicking on the *New* ▤ ▾ icon on the main tool bar. If you click the icon you will see the dialogue box shown in Fig. 2.1(a). Your list of available templates may be different.

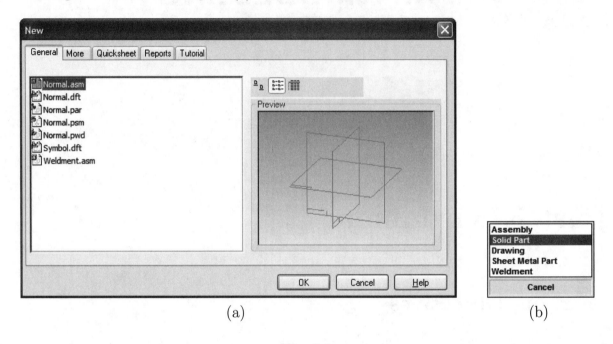

(a)   (b)

Fig. 2.1

□1 Click on the little black triangle to the right of the *New* ▤ ▾ icon. You will see Fig. 2.1(b).

□2 Click *Solid Part* on this menu to create a new part document using the default part template.

The default part template is set up with units and dimension style settings based on the whether *Metric* or *English* units were select during the installation.

To ensure you are using the necessary units and dimension standards, check the settings for the current part by doing the following:

□3 Click on *File→File Properties* in the menu bar.

□4 Click on the *Units* tab. See Fig. 2.2.

□5 Click on *Cancel*.

To check the dimension style do the following:

□6 Go to *Format→Style* on the menu bar.

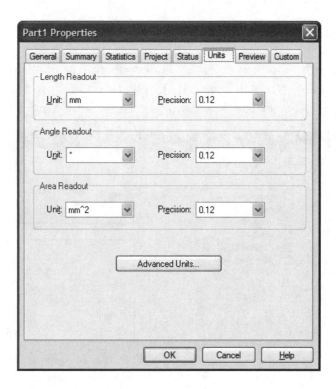

Fig. 2.2

7 Select *Dimension* from the *Style type* drop-down menu.

8 Select *Styles in use* from the *List* drop-down menu.

9 There should be one item, the default dimension style, listed in *Styles*. See Fig. 2.3. You may see *ANSI* or *ANSI (mm)* instead of *ISO* on your computer.

10 Click on *Cancel*.

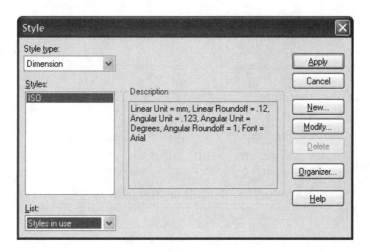

Fig. 2.3

If you find that either the units or the dimension style does not conform to your required needs or those used in your region you must find a template that contains the appropriate settings. To do so, close the current part document by selecting *File→Close* from the menu bar.

To select a template from which to create a new document click *File→New* in the menu bar. You will see the dialogue box in Fig. 2.1(a). The listed files are the default templates for Solid Edge environments. Select the *More* tab (see Fig. 2.4). Your list of templates on this

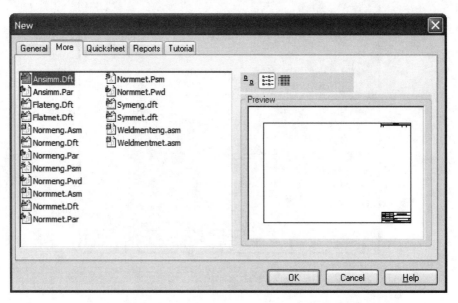

Fig. 2.4

tab may or may not resemble Fig. 2.4, depending on the options selected during the setup and installation of Solid Edge. Use Table 2.1 to select the appropriate template and then click *OK*. Note that *met* and *eng* in the template filename denote metric (SI) and English (imperial) units, respectively. If you are not sure which template to use choose *Ansimm.Par*.

Table 2.1

Template Name	*Default Units*	*Default Dimension Style*
Normal.par	Installation	Dependent
Ansimm.par	millimetres	ANSI
Normeng.par	inches	ANSI
Normmet.par	millimetres	ISO

2.2   User Interface

Assuming you have opened a new part document, your screen should resemble Fig. 2.5. In the titlebar at the top you should see the word *Part* following *Solid Edge V18*, indicating

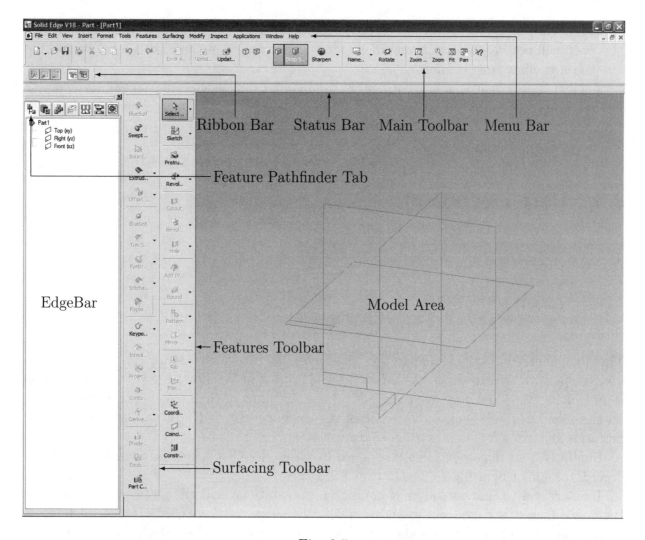

Fig. 2.5

that you are in the part environment. Before exploring the commands and capabilities of the part environment familiarize yourself with the user interface. It is composed of several elements shown in Fig. 2.5. These are described below.

- The *Model Area* is where the model of your part is displayed. When a new *part document* is created only the *Top*, *Right*, and *Front* reference planes are displayed.
- The *Menu Bar* contains all the Solid Edge menus. These change with the environment.
- On the *Main Toolbar* are icons for commands you will use frequently.
- The *EdgeBar* contains several tabs, including the *Feature Pathfinder*, to allow you to navigate your document. The EdgeBar can be displayed or hidden by clicking *Tools→EdgeBar* on the menu bar.
- The *Features Toolbar* is specific to the part environment. Initially, only the three reference planes are listed as features of your part. The commands on this toolbar add new features to your part. *Select Tool* select.. on the features toolbar allows you to select features of your part.

- The *Surfacing Toolbar* contains advanced commands. It is displayed by default but you will not be learning its commands in this manual. You can hide it by right-clicking on a toolbar and clicking *Surfacing*.
- The *Ribbon Bar* changes with each command to show you the currently available options and command steps.
- The *Status Bar* displays information and messages. It will prompt you for input when you are in a command.

2.3   Part Documents

Fig. 2.6

The document you have created in the part environment is called a part document. When saved, it has a *.par* extension. A saved part will appear in Windows Explorer with the icon shown in Fig. 2.6. You can save a part document with any of the following three commands on the menu bar: *File→Save*, *File→Save As*, or *File→Save All*. In addition, the ◫ icon performs the same function as *File→Save* using the menu bar.

Similarly, part documents can be opened by either double-clicking on their icons in Windows Explorer or by using *File→Open* in Solid Edge.

It is critical to understand that computer workstations and the software that runs on them are flawed and will occasionally crash. Because you know this is not an unusual occurrence, it is up to you to make sure you do not lose any current work as a consequence of a catastrophic software or hardware failure. The most effective action you can take is to save your files frequently to a location that will be unaffected by a system crash. Fortunately, Solid Edge has a feature that will automatically save your files on a regular basis. Fig. 2.7 illustrates one effective set of option settings that will cause Solid Edge to automatically save your files every 10 minutes.

1. Go to *Tools→Options* on the menu bar.
2. Select *Save*.
3. Change the settings in the dialogue box to resemble Fig. 2.7.
4. Click on *OK*.

It is highly recommended you do this. Furthermore, in your future employment as an engineer your work on the computer is your responsibility. If you lose your work because the computer crashes and you have not saved it properly, you will have to make up the lost work on your own time.

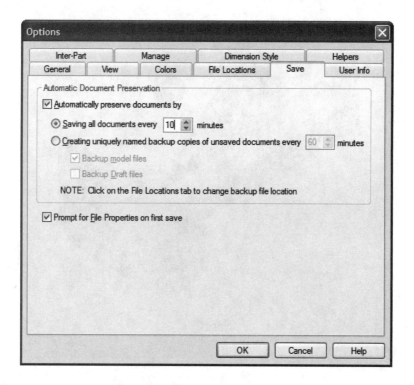

Fig. 2.7

2.4   Viewing

To learn how to change your view of a part, open the Solid Edge training file *anchor.par* normally located in *C:\Program Files\Solid Edge V18\Training*. On your computer Solid Edge may be installed elsewhere. If so, contact your administrator or instructor about where you can find this part document. Once you have opened it, your screen should look like Fig. 2.8.

1 Select *File→Open* from the menu bar.
2 Navigate to the *Training* folder.
3 Select *anchor.par*.
4 Click on *Open*.

Solid Edge allows you to dynamically change the view of your part without modifying the part itself. For example, you can rotate your viewpoint of the part (i.e., change the orientation of the part so that you are looking at the back of it). Solid Edge provides an array of these commands. The most common commands are listed below. Try them.

- *Visible Edges* ⊕ displays only the visible edges, and visible limiting elements of your part model (Fig. 2.9(a)).
- *Visible and Hidden Edges* ⊕ displays the same as above but hidden edges and hidden limiting elements are shown a shade lighter than the visible edges and visible limiting elements (Fig. 2.9(b)).
- *Shaded* ⬦ shades faces but edges are not shown (Fig. 2.9(c)).

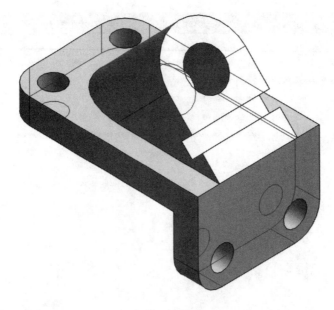

Fig. 2.8

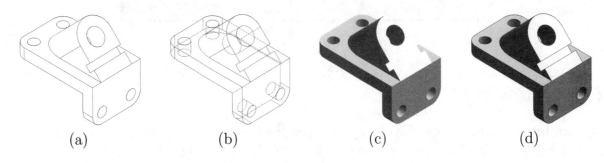

(a)   (b)   (c)   (d)

Fig. 2.9

- *Shaded with Visible Edges* 🗐 shades faces and visible edges, and visible limiting elements are drawn (Fig. 2.9(d)).

The second group of commands relates to changing the viewpoint of the display. The most common commands are listed below. Note that these commands can be accessed either from the main toolbar, from *View* on the menu bar, or by right-clicking in the model area.

- *Named Views* Name.. ˇ will change the viewpoint to the conventional top (horizontal), front (frontal), right side (profile), and iso (isometric) views of your model. The top, front, and right-side views correspond to the negative z-axis, negative y-axis, and x-axis directions. See Fig. 2.10(a) for the predefined views.

- *Rotate* Rotate allows you to rotate the part with respect to the centre of the display or about an axis. "Underneath" the rotate icon are three more commands. See Fig. 2.10(b).

- *Spin About* Spin A.. lets you spin your part about a face or normal axis to a face.

- *Look at Face* Look a.. rotates the part until the selected face is parallel to the picture plane.

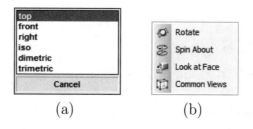

Fig. 2.10

- *Common Views* Comm.. allows you to select from all possible orthographic and isometric points of view.
- *Zoom Area* Zoom.. zooms into a portion of the drawing by clicking once in each of two diagonally opposed corners of the area of interest.
- *Zoom* Zoom enlarges or reduces the size of the view.
- *Fit* Fit sizes the view so that the entire part fits.
- *Pan* Pan moves the view of the part around the screen in the left-right, up-down directions of the display.

While these commands could be used in the middle of another command, you may find it more convenient to use your mouse as outlined in Table 2.2.

Table 2.2

Command	Using the Scroll Wheel	Without the Scroll Wheel
Rotate	Hold down the scroll wheel while moving the mouse.	Hold down the *Shift* key. Then hold down the right mouse button and move the mouse.
Zoom Area		Hold down the *Alt* key. Then hold down the right mouse button and move the mouse.
Zoom	Rotate the scroll wheel.	Hold down the *Ctrl* key. Then hold down the right mouse button and move the mouse.
Pan	Hold down the *Ctrl* key, the *Shift* key, and the scroll wheel while moving the mouse.	Hold down the *Ctrl* and *Shift* keys. Then hold down the right mouse button and move the mouse.

Note that Solid Edge displays the tangent edges like any other edge in the part environment. The rendering options of the current display can be modified from the menu bar with the following steps:

1. Click on *Format*→*Style* in the menu bar.
2. Modify the desired settings under the *Style type* drop-down menu.

3 Click on *Apply*.

4 Exit the dialogue box.

However, you are cautioned that some modifications may lead to an unacceptably slow display of your model.

If you find that the display of your part is slow, especially during rotation or zooming of the view, you should try reducing the sharpness using the *Sharpen* Sharpen (Fig. 2.11) icon on the main toolbar or try reducing the size of Solid Edge window.

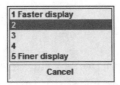

Fig. 2.11

2.5   Painting

Now we will try modifying the part — albeit in a superficial way. You can "paint" the faces of a part using the menu bar command *Format→Part Painter*. When you select this command your ribbon bar will change to the one shown in Fig. 2.12. Typically, when you select a command in Solid Edge you will be prompted for additional steps or options on the ribbon bar. Take a look at it. The *Style* item on this ribbon bar indicates what colour and texture you would like to apply. The *Select* drop-down menu allows you to narrow your selection to a specific type. Try the following and experiment with other options.

Fig. 2.12

1 Click on either the *Shaded* icon or *Shaded with Visible Edges* icon.

2 Click on *Format→Part Painter* from the menu bar.

3 Select *Black (Clear)* from the *Style* drop-down menu on the ribbon bar.

4 Select *Face* from the *Select* drop-down menu on the ribbon bar.

5 Move your mouse pointer over the part in the model area and select one or more faces.

The entire part painted in *Black (Clear)* will resemble Fig. 2.13.

The part painter is helpful in marking features and faces of your part and generating photo-realistic renderings of your part. Beware that some features use colour to indicate special properties of a face such as threads which use green.

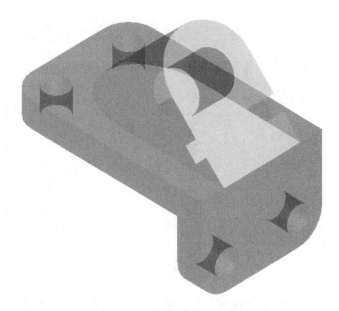

Fig. 2.13

2.6 Rendering a Bitmap

Once you have painted your part, you may wish to create a bitmap file containing a view of your part. Bitmaps, stored in JPEG files or similar formats, are useful for inclusion in reports and presentations, or publishing on the web. However, saving a bitmap does not save your part. You can neither modify your part nor change its view using a bitmap file.

When working in Solid Edge, rendering parameters such as lighting, background, anti-aliasing, and rendering mode are set by default so that your display is as fast as possible while still providing you with the visual information you need. If you wish to save a bitmap of your part, then these parameters can be adjusted to create a better or even photo-realistic rendering at the expense of rendering time.

To create a detailed rendered bitmap of a part, first create a 3D view style and then save the bitmap file. To create the 3D view style:

1 Click on *Format→Style* in the menu bar.

2 Select *3D View Styles* under *Style type* in the dialogue box (Fig. 2.14).

3 Click on *New*.

4 Next to the label *Name* give your new 3D view style a name (Fig. 2.15).

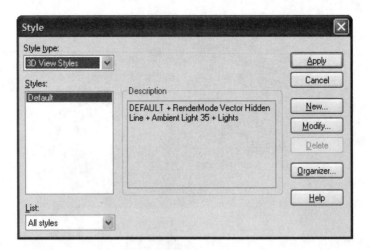

Fig. 2.14

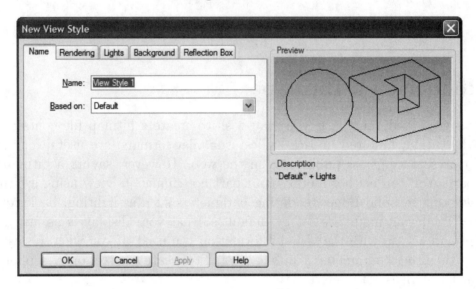

Fig. 2.15

5. Experiment with the other tabs and options.

6. Click on *OK* to save your new 3D view style.

To save a bitmap of your part using the new 3D view style you just created follow these steps.

1. Click on *File→Save As Image* in the menu bar.

2. You will see Fig. 2.16. Here you must select your file type. Give your file a name by typing it next to the label *Filename*. Then select *JPEG Image* from the *Save as type* drop-down menu.

3. Next click on *Options* and select the 3D view style you created earlier from the *Alternate view style* drop-down menu. See Fig. 2.17.

4. Click on *OK*.

5. Click on *Save* to create the bitmap.

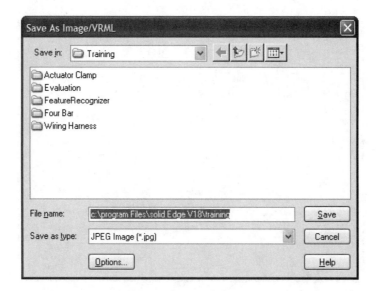

Fig. 2.16

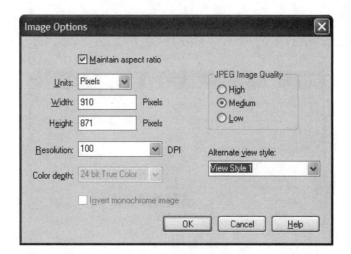

Fig. 2.17

This will create a reasonably small file. It is not recommended that you use *Windows Bitmap* (*.bmp*) or *TIFF Image* (*.tif*) since these formats require a great deal of space.

Note that the last displayed position, orientation, and zoom of your part in the model area will be used to render the image. Creating the bitmap may take several minutes depending on the 3D view style options you selected.

2.7   Inspection

Another action you can perform on a part is to query it for its properties or to measure it. Follow these steps to obtain the physical properties of a part.

1   Select the menu bar command *Inspect→Physical Properties*.

2   Select *Change* (Fig. 2.18).

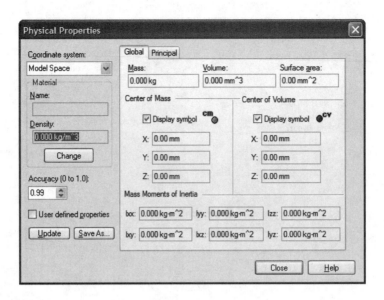

Fig. 2.18

<u>3</u> Click on the *Value* next to *Density* and type *1* (Fig. 2.19).

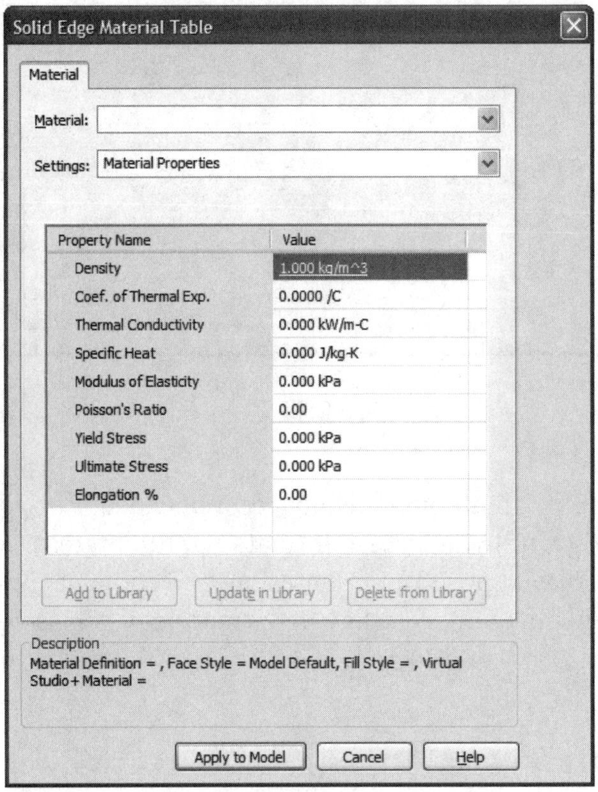

Fig. 2.19

<u>4</u> Click on *Apply to Model.*

$\boxed{5}$ Return to the *Physical Properties* dialogue box by selecting the menu bar command *Inspect→Physical Properties* again.

$\boxed{6}$ Set the *Accuracy* to 1 (Fig. 2.20).

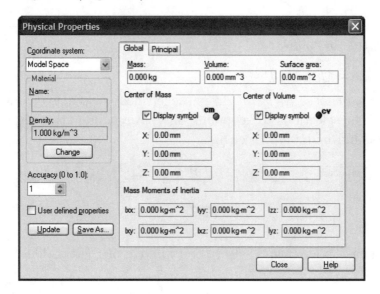

Fig. 2.20

$\boxed{7}$ Click on the *Update* button.

You will see that on the *Global* and *Principal* tabs newly computed physical properties are displayed (Fig. 2.21). The physical properties will be a good way to compare the part models you draw from drawings in later chapters to the solutions. For two parts to be identical their volumes, surface areas, and all three radii of gyration must be the same.

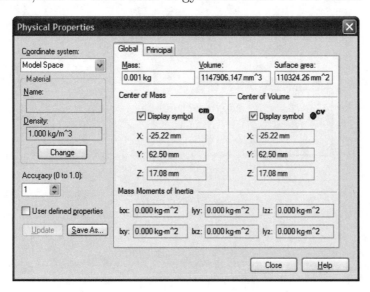

Fig. 2.21

Another source of information is measurements that can be extracted from your part using the following menu bar commands.

- *Inspect→Measure Distance*,
- *Inspect→Measure Minimum Distance*,
- *Inspect→Normal Distance*, and
- *Inspect→Measure Angle*.

As an example try the following:

[1] Click on *Inspect→Measure Distance*.

[2] In the ribbon bar choose *Keypoints* from the leftmost drop-down menu (Fig. 2.22). This will restrict your selections to keypoints only. Keypoints typically include endpoints, centre points, and midpoints of edges.

Fig. 2.22

[3] Move your mouse pointer and select the top edge of the two like holes of the *anchor* part (Fig. 2.23).

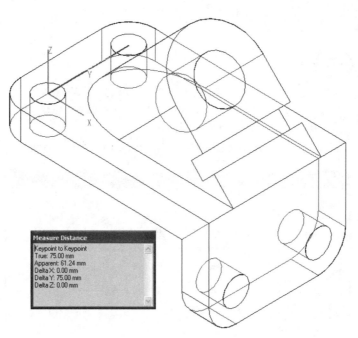

Fig. 2.23

4. Click on *Reset* on the ribbon bar to select another pair of features for measurement.

5. Click on *Close* on the ribbon bar to exit the command.

The other measurement commands work in a similar manner. You will find the measurement commands useful to verify that you have completed exercises in later chapters correctly.

Exercises

1. This exercise is intended to test your understanding of the material discussed in this chapter. Open *Body01.par* in *C:\Program Files\Solid Edge V18\Training* (or equivalent directory on your computer) and do the following.

   (a) Measure the "height" of the object when viewed using the *iso* named view.

   (b) What is the direction of the third principal axis?

   (c) Create a JPEG bitmap file of the part with the following specifications. Rendering may take several minutes.

   - Part colour: All *Steel* except the cylindrical faces of all holes are to be *Black (dull)*.
   - Rendering: Anti-alias level should be *High* and render mode should be *Smooth Shaded*.
   - Background: All *White*.
   - Part Orientation: All of the part should be visible; it should be in isometric view such that the base of the part is on the bottom. When first opened, the part is upside down.

2. If you created a new design in Solid Edge, what would you submit for grading: the part document or bitmap? Why?

3. Open *bolt01.par* in *C:\Program Files\Solid Edge V18\Training* (or equivalent directory on your computer). This part was created in SI units. Change the units of *Length* and *Area* in *File→File Properties→Units* to inches. Change the units of *Density*, *Volume*, and *Mass* in *File→File Properties→Units→Advanced Units* to inches and pounds. Does changing the units change the actual length of the part? Measure the part to verify. Does changing the units change the surface area, volume, and radii of gyration?

4. Why are two of the three radii of gyration of *bearing.par* in *C:\Program Files\ Solid Edge V18\Training* (or equivalent directory on your computer) the same?

Features

Learning Objectives

After completing this chapter, you will be able to:

1. Define "feature."
2. Define "profile."
3. Create and modify profiles.
4. Create protrusions, cutouts, revolved protrusions, revolved cutouts, and thin wall features.
5. Use the select tool and QuickPick.

In this chapter, you will be introduced to features, which are the building blocks of parts. You will learn how to use a few of the most commonly used features to add volume to a part and subtract volume from a part. The exercises at the end of the chapter will test your ability to read an isometric pictorial with dimensions and construct parts using the features you have learned in this chapter.

3.1 Features

In Solid Edge, parts are constructed by creating features. A feature either adds volume to the part, subtracts volume from the part, modifies existing features, repeats features, or has no effect at all on the design body. All features are listed on the *Feature Pathfinder* tab of the *EdgeBar* (Fig. 2.5). Looking at Fig. 3.1, the features that make up this part are listed on the *EdgeBar* beginning with *Top (xy)* and ending with *Cutout 1*.

When you create a new part, Solid Edge will automatically provide you with three default features named: *Top (xy)*, *Right (yz)*, and *Front (xz)*. These construction geometry features are called references planes. They do not contribute to the shape of your design body but are needed to construct further features. If you move your mouse pointer over a feature in either the EdgeBar or in the model area, it will be highlighted in red (Fig. 3.2).

To construct a new feature, you must select a command on the *Features Toolbar* (Fig. 2.5). Once completed, the feature will be added to the list of features in the *Feature Pathfinder*.

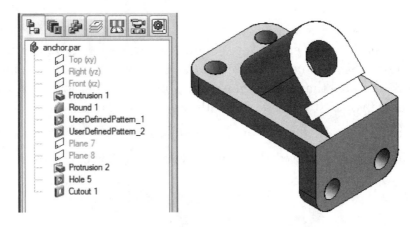

Fig. 3.1

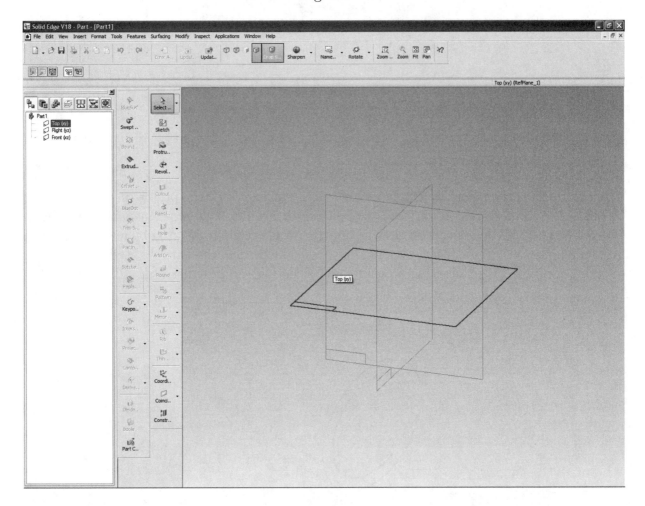

Fig. 3.2

3.2 First Feature

With a new part, there are a limited number of features that you can choose to be the first. At the top of the *Features Toolbar*, you see that only the *Sketch* Sketch, *Protrusion* Protru.., and

Revolved Protrusion Revol.. icons are not greyed out. This is because these features create a new volume rather than modify an existing volume. They are **additive** features. If you look closely at the icons for *Sketch* and *Revolved Protrusion* you will notice a small black triangle on the right. This indicates that the given icon has hidden "underneath" it additional icons. This is known as a flyout. To access the additional icons on a flyout, click on the black triangle on the right of the *Sketch* Sketch or *Revolved Protrusion* Revol.. icon to reveal the *Sketch* flyout (Fig. 3.3(a) Revol..) or *Revolved Protrusion* flyout (Fig. 3.3(b)), respectively.

| | (a) | | | (b) |

Fig. 3.3

3.3 Protrusion Feature

A **protrusion** is the most often-used feature. It is a prism: a closed profile on a plane swept through space in a direction normal to the sketch or profile. The two-dimensional profile in Fig. 3.4 is made of two concentric circles, and the profile plane is denoted by a square. When protruded, the two concentric circles form a tube. The protrusion feature entails three steps: selecting a profile plane, creating a profile, and selecting the protrusion depth.

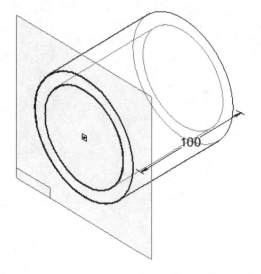

Fig. 3.4

1 Create a new part.

[2] Click on *Protrusion*

The SmartStep ribbon bar appears as shown in Fig. 3.5. For each command the ribbon bar is unique. It indicates the steps you must complete to create the feature you have chosen. For the protrusion feature there are five steps:

Fig. 3.5

1. *Plane or Sketch Step* — Select the plane on which you will draw the profile.
2. *Draw Profile Step* — Create the profile.
3. *Side Step* — Select the side of the profile plane where you will protrude the profile.
4. *Extent Step* — Select the depth of the protrusion.
5. *Treatment Step* — Special options.

The second- through to the fifth-step icons are greyed out because you must complete the first step before you may continue on the others. Also notice that the status bar prompts you for the action you must take for the current step. Your status bar should read: *Click on a planar face or reference plane. To change the Create-From option, click on the list.*

With the protrusion feature, you can create the simplest primitives such as cubes, blocks, wedges, cylinders, tubes, and prisms of high complexity (Fig. 3.6).

Fig. 3.6

3.3.1   Cylinder

For your first protrusion you will create a cylinder. At this point, you must complete the first step: choose a plane or sketch. For the first feature in your part you will normally select one of the reference planes by either clicking on it in the EdgeBar or in the model area.

[3] Click on one of the reference planes.

You will be immediately whisked into the **profile view**. The ribbon bar and features bar will be replaced. Your screen should appear as shown in Fig. 3.7. Solid Edge has rotated your viewpoint such that the profile plane you just selected is parallel the computer screen.

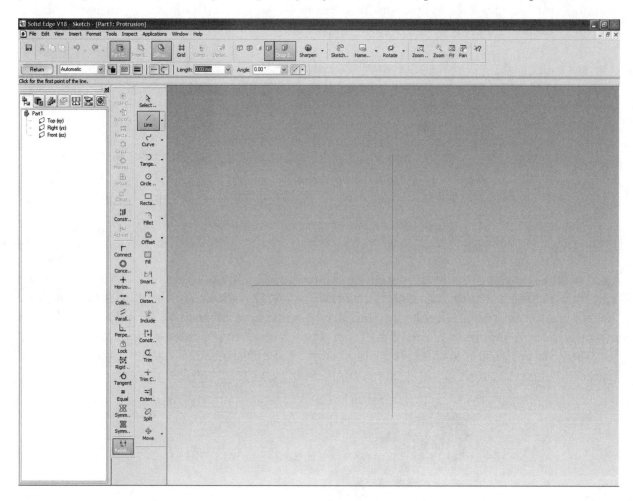

Fig. 3.7

To complete this step successfully and proceed to the next protrusion steps you must complete a correct profile. A **profile** is a closed chain or loop of edges. A circle is the simplest example of a profile.

4 Click on *Circle by Center* ⊙ Circle .. on the *Draw Toolbar*.

5 Click anywhere in the *model area* to locate the centre of your circle.

6 Click on another point in the *model area* to set the radius, or type a radius or diameter in the appropriate box in the ribbon bar.

If you do not type the units following the number, the default units will be assumed. Now you have a simple, complete profile. Your profile should resemble Fig. 3.8.

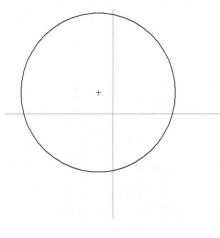

Fig. 3.8

⑦ Click on *Return* on the ribbon bar.

You will be returned to the part environment and forwarded to the extent step. Note that the side step has been skipped. The side step allows you to choose the side of your profile (inside or outside) on which the material of your protrusion will be placed. Solid Edge has automatically selected the inside since the alternative, outside, would result in a solid with infinite volume, which is patently impractical. In the extent step, you must choose a depth for your protrusion feature. The model area should resemble Fig. 3.9.

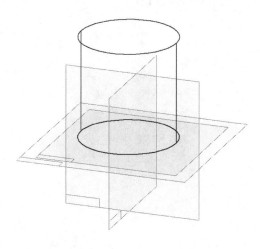

Fig. 3.9

⑧ Move your mouse pointer over your profile in the model area.

As you move your mouse back and forth you will see that a red outline of the protrusion is displayed. Clicking will specify the depth as displayed by the red outline. You can also select the *Distance* in the ribbon bar by typing in a number and optional units.

⑨ Type a *Distance* greater than zero in the ribbon bar.

Then, in the model area, you will have to choose on which side of the profile plane the protrusion will be extended.

[10] Make your choice by clicking.

Your design model should resemble Fig. 3.10.

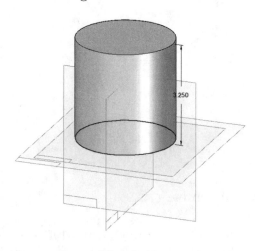

Fig. 3.10

You are now at the treatment step. For this explanation we are not interested in any of the treatment options. Click on *Finish* on the ribbon toolbar to complete your first feature. Your design model should resemble Fig. 3.11.

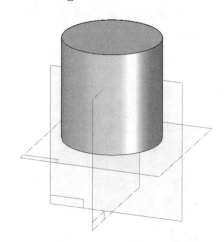

Fig. 3.11

3.3.2   Triangular Prism

Now you will create a protrusion with a triangular profile that will result in a triangular prism. To begin, delete the first feature.

[1] Click on *Select Tool* ᴎselect.. at the top of the features toolbar.

2 Select the cylindrical protrusion feature by clicking on it in either the EdgeBar or in the model area.

3 Press *Delete* on your keyboard.

Only the three reference planes should remain in your list of features.

4 Start a new protrusion feature.

5 Select one of the reference planes for your profile plane to get to the draw profile step.

Now you will use the *Line Command* Line to create a triangle. Before you do that, hide the reference planes, which appear as the horizontal and vertical blue lines in your model area.

6 Click on *Select Tool* Select...

7 Right-click in the model area and select *Hide All→Reference Planes* from the menu that appears.

8 Now select *Line* Line from the draw toolbar.

9 Click somewhere near the centre of the model area.

This will start the profile. Each time you now click you will add one line to your profile.

10 Click twice to create two lines in a chain.

Your profile should resemble Fig. 3.12.

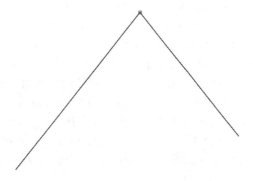

Fig. 3.12

Make sure you do not select collinear points. To close the profile you must:

11 Move your mouse pointer over the first line you created until it is highlighted in red.

12 Keep moving your mouse pointer while also maintaining the red highlight on the first line.

Next to the mouse pointer (which appears as cross-hairs) you will see one of three tiny icons. The first icon you are likely to see (⟋) indicates that if you click at this point you will ensure the endpoint of the line segment you create will be somewhere on the highlighted line. If you click when you see the midpoint icon (⟍) you will ensure that the line segment ends at the midpoint of the first line. Similarly, if you click when you see the endpoint icon (⟋) you ensure that the endpoint of the line segment is connected to the endpoint of the first line.

[13] Connect the endpoint of the third line segment to the first point of your profile.

If you click anywhere else you will have created an invalid profile. In such a case, select *Edit→Undo* from the menu bar and try again. Your profile should resemble Fig. 3.13.

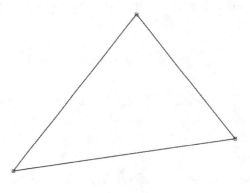

Fig. 3.13

A valid profile must contain at least one complete loop of edges. Fig. 3.14 illustrates a few invalid profiles and Fig. 3.15 illustrates a few valid profiles. A valid profile is a loop or chain of edges. The edges may be line segments or segments of a curve. So far, you have only seen line segments but a profile can also include circular arcs, elliptical arcs, and more advanced general curves such as B-splines. For these edges to form a valid profile a few conditions must be met. First, the endpoint of every edge must be connected to the endpoint of one and only one other edge. As a consequence, the profile will be closed. Second, the profile must not self-intersect. That is, no two edges may intersect. Third, where each pair of edges meet there must be a connect constraint present. In Fig. 3.15, you will see that there is a small black box where the pairs of edges meet. This is a *Connect Relationship* handle. If you do not see these handles, ensure that there is check mark next to the menu bar item *Tools→Relationship Handles*. It ensures the endpoints of the adjacent edges meet. If any of these requirements are not met Solid Edge will not allow you to complete the draw profile step. You will be forced to correct the profile or save the profile geometry as a sketch, thus aborting your current feature but without losing the invalid profile. Look at Fig. 3.14 to see if you can determine why the given profiles are invalid.

When you used the line command to create the triangular profile, Solid Edge automatically added the connect relationships, which are indicated by black box handles.

[14] Click on *Return*.

With the cylinder you could protrude your profile on the other side of the profile plane. However, you can protrude a profile an equal distance on both sides of the profile plane by selecting the *Symmetric Extent* ▦ icon on the ribbon toolbar and then selecting a distance in the *Distance* box on the ribbon bar.

[15] Click on *Symmetric Extent* ▦ in the ribbon bar.

The model area should look like Fig. 3.16.

[16] Type a *Distance* in the ribbon bar greater than zero.

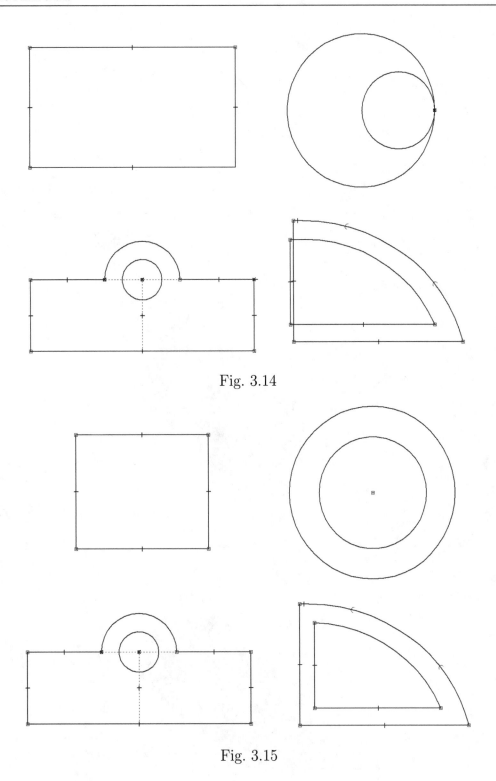

Fig. 3.14

Fig. 3.15

Note that the distance you type is the overall depth of the protrusion, not the distance on one side of the profile plane. The model area should look like Fig. 3.17.

[17] Click on *Finish*.

Your profile should resemble Fig. 3.18.

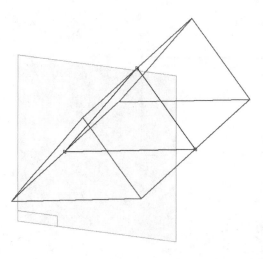

Fig. 3.16

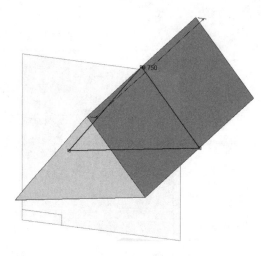

Fig. 3.17

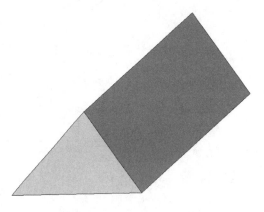

Fig. 3.18

Observe now that on the features toolbar none of the icons is greyed out. This is because many features require at least one existent feature to act on. Try the protrusion feature again, but this time select one of the faces of your triangular prism as the profile plane instead of a reference plane. Your profile plane may be any reference plane or planar face. You may not select curved faces.

3.3.3   Protrusion with Complex Profile

For this protrusion, you will draw a profile based on Fig. 3.19. Examine this figure carefully. It is fully dimensioned.

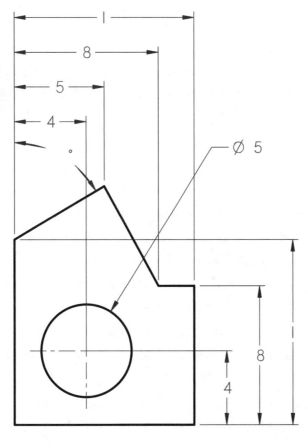

Fig. 3.19

1. Create a new part.
2. Begin the protrusion feature.
3. Select one of the reference planes as the profile plane for the protrusion feature.
4. Hide the reference planes.
5. Click on the line command in the profile view.
6. Click somewhere in the profile plane to begin a line.
7. Type the length of the line in the *Length* text box on the ribbon bar (Fig. 3.20).

By moving your mouse pointer around the model area you will see that the length of your line is constrained but its angle is not. You want to select a horizontal angle. To do so exactly, move your mouse pointer around until your line is approximately horizontal.

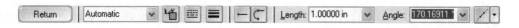

Fig. 3.20

8 Click when you see the horizontal relationship indicator icon (▬) next to your mouse pointer. See Fig. 3.21.

Fig. 3.21

If you did this correctly, you will see a small black vertical line in the middle of your line segment as shown in Fig. 3.22. This is a *Horizontal/Vertical* ╂) relationship handle indicating that your line is horizontal or vertical relative to the current profile plane axes.

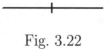

Fig. 3.22

If you did not get this handle, try again by either undoing the line or deleting it. To delete it, click on the *Select Tool* select.. icon at the top of the draw toolbar, then select the line and press the *Delete* key. If you find that your line is very small or too large relative to your model area, click on the *Zoom Area* zoom.. icon or *Zoom* zoom icon to change the visible area of your model to something more appropriate.

9 Restart the line command by clicking on it again.

10 Starting from the bottom right corner, add the remaining lines of the outside profile except for the leftmost vertical line.

Do not worry about the lengths of the lines. Ensure that when you create the two vertical lines and one remaining horizontal line Solid Edge recognizes them as such and attaches the horizontal/vertical constraint (indicated by its handle) to those line segments. Try to draw the profile approximately as shown. The closer your profile is to the final shape, the easier it will be to complete it.

11 Complete the outside profile by adding the leftmost vertical line.

When you get to the second oblique line you will notice that in order to make the last line segment vertical you will have to choose the endpoint of the second oblique line to be directly above your start point. To do this you will have to use an *Alignment Indicator*. Move your mouse pointer over the start point of the profile. Pause for a moment. Now carefully move your mouse pointer directly up and you will see a dashed line extending from the point over which you hovered your mouse pointer (Fig. 3.23). Without losing the alignment indicator (the dashed line), click when your mouse pointer is at the desired height. If you do not see the alignment indicator's dashed line ensure that *Tools→Alignment Indicator* has a check mark next to it in the menu bar. Your profile should resemble Fig. 3.24.

Now you will add the linear and angular dimensions shown in Fig. 3.19.

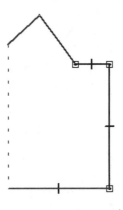

Fig. 3.23

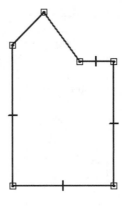

Fig. 3.24

[12] Click on *SmartDimension* smart.. on the draw toolbar.

[13] Then click on the lower horizontal line.

[14] Click to locate the dimension.

It does not matter where you put it, but it is advisable to put it outside the profile so things do not become cluttered.

[15] Type your dimension number — *1* — and press *Enter*. See Fig. 3.25.

[16] Add two vertical dimensions of lengths .8 and 1 by selecting the right-hand and left-hand vertical lines, respectively.

[17] Add the horizontal length .5 and length .8 dimensions.

For each horizontal dimension, first select the left-hand vertical line. When making the second selection you may notice that you can select the entire line, the midpoint on the line, or an endpoint of the line. Each of these is indicated as before by a small indicator icon next to the mouse pointer. For each horizontal dimension choose the endpoint corresponding to right-hand end of the dimension. Now, where you click to place the dimension has a bearing on whether it will measure a horizontal or vertical distance. Move your mouse pointer around until you see a vertical dimension and click. Type your dimension as before. Your profile with vertical and horizontal dimensions should appear as shown in Fig. 3.26.

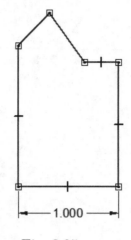

Fig. 3.25

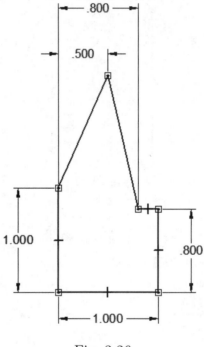

Fig. 3.26

The last dimension to add for the outer profile is the 60°. This can be done using the same tool as above.

18 Start the *SmartDimension* smart.. command.

19 Click on the leftmost vertical line.

20 Click on the oblique line connected to the leftmost vertical line.

21 Click on *Angle* on the ribbon toolbar.

22 Click to place the dimension.

23 Type the dimension value — either 60 or 120, depending on where you located the angle dimension.

The outside profile is complete (Fig. 3.27). Create the inside profile — the circle — locating and sizing it as shown in Fig. 3.19.

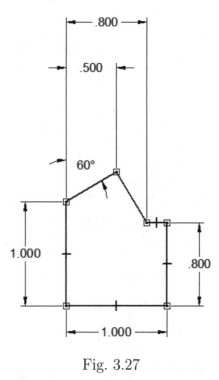

Fig. 3.27

24 Use *Circle by Center* Circle.. to create a circle.

25 Dimension its diameter using *SmartDimension* Smart...

26 Dimension its location both horizontally and vertically.

Your profile should appear as shown in Fig. 3.28.

In summary, create profiles using the following steps:

1. Place one edge belonging to the profile and dimension it. This will provide you with a rough idea of the scale of the profile. Zoom to fit if needed.
2. Add the remaining edges that you need. Ensure the profile is valid.
3. Add the dimensions.

What may happen as you add dimensions is that your profile becomes twisted beyond recognition. This is not uncommon. Two ways to deal with this problem are either to undo the last dimension and proceed by adding dimensions in a new order or to reshape the profile. To reshape it, click the select tool and then click on an edge in your profile. Little filled black squares will appear at various places on the edge. Click and drag one of the squares to reshape the element.

The lengths of line segments and of the radius or diameter of a circle can be specified either by selecting the edge and typing in the appropriate box of the ribbon bar or by attaching a dimension. You are very strongly advised to use the *SmartDimension* tool and not to rely on the former method. The former method allows you to specify what Solid Edge considers

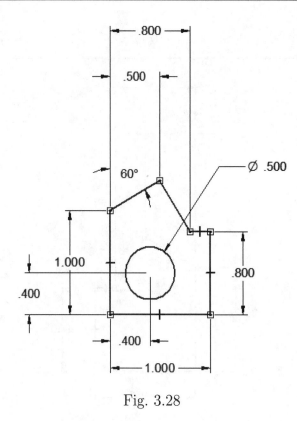

Fig. 3.28

an **initial value**. That is, when you add dimensions initial values of adjacent edges may be modified. Consequently, you cannot rely on initial values. So why use dimensions at all? You will learn that for simple profiles like the one in Fig. 3.19 you may be able to get away with using initial values only. However, in other instances this will lead to incorrect results, especially when other types of relationships (not yet covered) are involved. More details will be provided in Chapter 4. As well, relationships other than connect and horizontal/vertical will be introduced.

27 Click on *Return* to go to the extent step.

28 Complete the protrusion using a protrusion depth of 1 unit.

This will yield the solid shown in Fig. 3.29. If you have done this correctly, the physical properties of your design model should be exactly those shown in Table 3.1 in the default units of your part.

Table 3.1

Volume		0.84912 unit^3
Surface Area		7.4981 unit^2
	K1	0.45834 unit
Radii of Gyration	K2	0.45374 unit
	K3	0.40308 unit

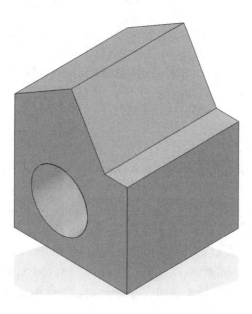

Fig. 3.29

The inner profile — the circle — forms a hole in your profile. You may create multiple profiles as long as they are independent, non-intersecting closed profiles. If the profiles do not touch or intersect, the profiles will alternate between solid and void like the example. Inside the outer profile is solid material and inside the inner profile is a void. If there was another profile inside the circle that neither touched nor intersected the circle, it would be solid when protruded. If you create several profiles that intersect or touch, Solid Edge will protrude a solid that is an outline of the outermost extents of all the profiles.

Earlier, you learned that you can specify a distance and on which side(s) of the profile plane the protrusion will extend. These options are discussed below.

- The *Through All* ⊞ extent option is not normally used with additive features since it specifies an infinite extent distance.
- *Through Next* ⊞ extends the protrusion to the next surface. If the surface only partially obstructs the protrusion, the feature will fail with this option.
- *From/To Extent* ⊞ selects two faces that bound the start and end of the protrusion.
- The *Finite Extent* ⊞ option was illustrated above. A fixed protrusion distance is specified.

Note that it is possible to start a protrusion in the middle of an existing feature by, for example, selecting a reference plane in the middle of an existing feature as the profile plane. When the next protrusion is complete it is effectively added to the existing feature. Where they overlap, the density and volume of the part are unaffected.

Equally important are methods you need to use to select the profile plane when beginning a protrusion. Although there are nine options for selecting a profile plane from the *Create-From Options* drop-down menu box on the ribbon bar, only the first three are commonly used.

- *Coincident Plane* ▱ — Select a planar face or reference plane as the profile plane.

- *Parallel Plane* ⌖ — Select a profile plane parallel to an existing planar face or reference plane.
- *Angled Plane* ⌖ — Select a profile plane at an angle to a planar face or reference plane.
- *Perpendicular Plane* ⌖ — Select a profile plane perpendicular to a face or reference plane.
- *Coincident Plane by Axis* ⌖ — Select a planar face or reference plane as profile plane oriented with a specified axis. Unlike the *Coincident Plane* option, you can select the orientation of the profile plane, which will affect the direction of horizontal/vertical in the profile plane.
- *Plane Normal to Curve* ⌖ — Create a profile plane intersecting a curve and that is normal to the direction of the curve's tangent at that point.
- *Plane by 3 Points* ⌖ — Create a profile plane by selecting three points.
- *Feature's Plane* ⌖ — Select the profile plane of an existing feature.
- *Last Plane* ⌖ — Select the last profile plane created or used.

3.4   Cutout

The **cutout** feature, started by clicking the ⌖ Cutout icon, removes a volume corresponding to a profile translated through space in a direction normal to the profile plane. This operation is like creating a protrusion but performing a Boolean subtraction to remove its swept volume from the existing features instead of performing a Boolean union. Obviously, this feature cannot be the first feature of a part. Typically, you will use a cutout to remove a three-dimensional volume in the shape of a hole, slot, or similar feature. Fig. 3.30 shows an example of a cutout feature including the profile plane and profile. The profile is composed of three lines in a "U" shape.

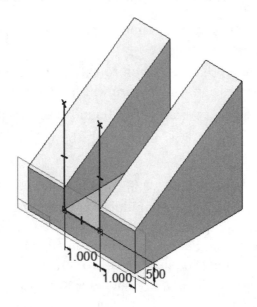

Fig. 3.30

A cutout feature involves the same steps as a protrusion feature:

1. *Plane or Sketch Step* 📦,
2. *Draw Profile Step* 🖊,
3. *Side Step* 📄,
4. *Extent Step* 🔖, and
5. *Treatment Step* 📦.

A cutout feature always begins with selecting a profile plane in the *Plane or Sketch Step*. This is identical to the protrusion feature. However, unlike the protrusion feature, a profile drawn in the *Draw Profile Step* does not have to be closed unless there is more than one. An example of an open profile is shown in Fig. 3.31(a). It results in the part shown in either Fig. 3.31(b) or Fig. 3.31(c). In the cutout, the side step determines on which side of an open profile the material is removed. The remaining steps are identical to the protrusion feature.

As an example, you will create the part shown in Fig. 3.32(a). This part can be created by only employing protrusions but that is the hard way to draw this design in Solid Edge. Note that if you try to create this part in the manner shown in Fig. 3.33 (using only protrusions and no cutouts), you will get a part that is incorrect because it differs where the wedge meets the cylinder. In the first step, Fig. 3.33(a), the protrusion's profile is a circle drawn on the front plane. In the second step, Fig. 3.33(b), the protrusion's profile is a circle with a rectangular area removed drawn in a plane parallel to the front plane. In the last step, Fig. 3.33(c), the protrusion's profile is a triangle drawn in a plane parallel to the right plane.

The part in Fig. 3.32(a) can be drawn using only two features: a protrusion and a cutout with only a circle and a line as their respective profiles.

1. Start a protrusion feature.
2. Select the *Front* reference plane as the profile plane.
3. Hide the reference planes.
4. Draw a circle.
5. Dimension the circle with the *SmartDimension* tool. Type *3in*, denoting three inches, as the diameter.

It does not matter where the circle is in the profile plane. Your profile should look like Fig. 3.34.

6. Give the protrusion a depth of 5 inches.
7. Finish the protrusion feature.

Your protrusion should appear as shown in Fig. 3.35.

Now create a cutout feature. You want the profile plane parallel to the right plane and intersecting the axis of the cylinder you just created.

8. Begin the *Cutout* 🔲 cutout feature by clicking on the icon.

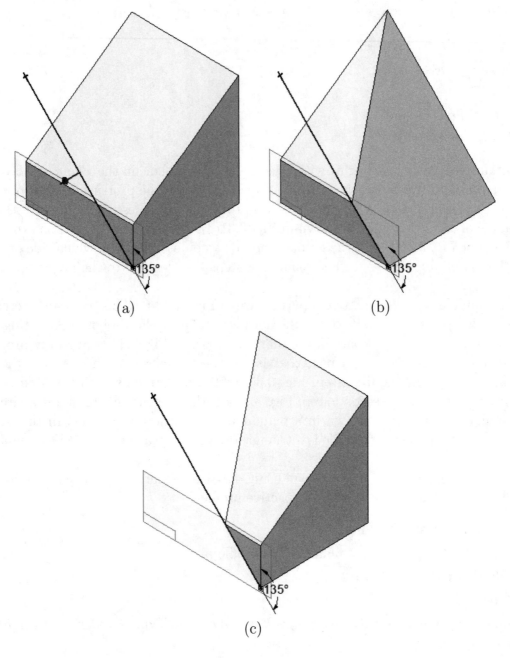

Fig. 3.31

9 In the *Plane or Sketch Step* choose *Parallel Plane* from the *Create-From Options* pull-down menu on the ribbon bar.

10 Click on *Right* reference plane in the *Feature Pathfinder*.

Now that you have selected which plane your profile will be parallel to, you must select an element that it will intersect.

11 Click on *Keypoints* on the ribbon bar.

12 Click on *Circle Center* .

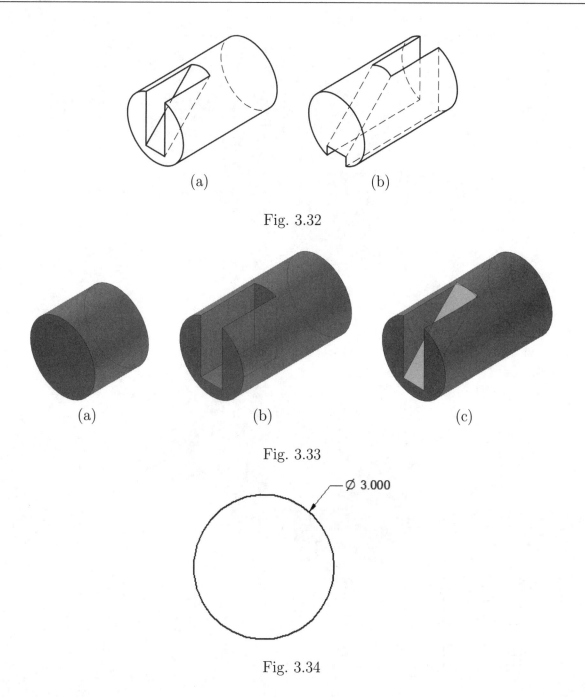

Fig. 3.32

Fig. 3.33

Fig. 3.34

You have selected the option to use the centre of a circle as the element your profile plane must intersect.

13 Select either of the two circles of the cylinder. This will take you to *Draw Profile Step*.

Before you click on a circle your model area should look like Fig. 3.36.

14 In the profile view, draw the profile in Fig. 3.37.

The profile is a single line running from a midpoint at the top of the cylinder at a 45° angle to the horizontal. The length of the line does not matter. The profile does not have to be closed. One inch is a sufficient length.

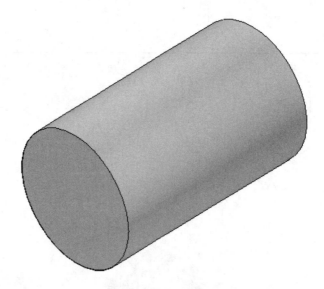

Fig. 3.35

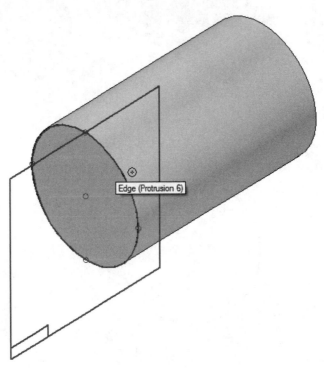

Edge (Protrusion 6)

Fig. 3.36

15 Click on *Return* to go to the side step.

Here you will choose on which side of your profile material will be removed from your model. The direction the arrow is pointing indicates the side from which material will be removed. If you click when the arrow appears as shown in Fig. 3.38(a) you will get the part shown in Fig. 3.32(a). If you click when the arrow appears as shown in Fig. 3.38(b) you will get the part shown in Fig. 3.32(b).

16 Select the extent shown in Fig. 3.38(a).

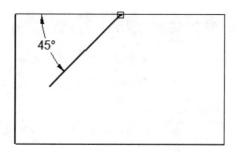

Fig. 3.37

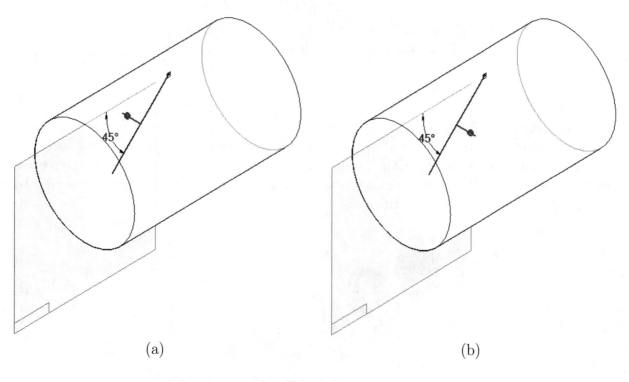

(a)   (b)

Fig. 3.38

17 Select *Symmetric Extent* from the ribbon bar.

18 Enter an extent *Distance* of *1in* on the ribbon bar.

19 Click on *Finish* to complete the feature.

A common problem with cutouts is that a given cutout does not change the part. In such a case, Solid Edge will not allow you to proceed with completing the cutout feature. You will see the dialogue box in Fig. 3.39. You must either change the feature so that it does modify the part or cancel the feature altogether.

3.5 Revolved Protrusion Feature

The *Revolved Protrusion* Revol.. command constructs a feature that is very similar to the protrusion feature. It adds volume to a part even if no features yet exist in the part. The

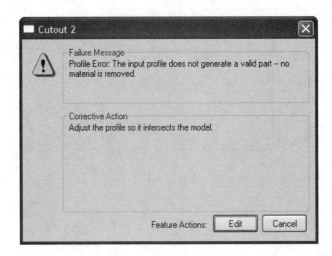

Fig. 3.39

revolved protrusion differs in that the path of protrusion is along a circular arc normal to the profile plane. To specify the protrusion path, an axis of revolution must be selected in the profile plane. In other words, the profile is swept about the axis of revolution to create a revolved protrusion. Fig. 3.40 shows a sphere, a torus, a cone, a cylinder, and a tube created by a revolved protrusion sharing the same axis of revolution.

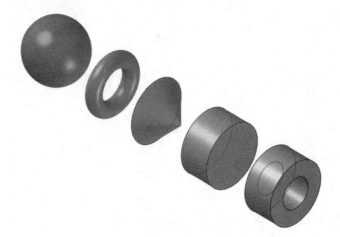

Fig. 3.40

The SmartStep ribbon bar for the revolved protrusion is shown in Fig. 3.41. These break down as follows:

1. *Plane or Sketch Step* ▣,
2. *Draw Profile Step* ▣,
3. *Side Step* ▣, and
4. *Extent Step* ▣.

Since you are familiar with these steps from the protrusion feature, three examples follow to elucidate the use of the revolved protrusion feature.

Fig. 3.41

3.5.1   Sphere

A revolved feature can be used to construct a sphere, a hemisphere, or part of a sphere. Create the sphere shown in Fig. 3.42(a).

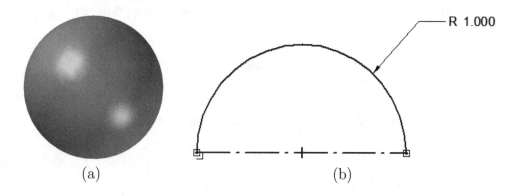

(a)   (b)

Fig. 3.42

[1] Create a new part.

[2] Click on *Revolved Protrusion* Revol...

[3] Select the *Right* reference plane as the profile plane.

Draw the profile shown in Fig. 3.42(b).

[4] Draw a line in the profile view.

[5] Draw a 180° circular arc with the *Tangent Arc* Tange.. command connected to the ends of the line.

You will notice that in Fig. 3.42(b) Solid Edge has placed a perpendicular relationship between the arc and line on the left side to ensure that the arc is 180°.

[6] Dimension the arc.

[7] Select the line to be the axis of revolution using the *Axis of Revolution* Axis of.. command.

[8] Click on *Return*.

You should be in the extent step because for a closed profile such as your semicircle the solid part of your protrusion will always be on the inside of the profile. You will see the ribbon bar shown in Fig. 3.43. For a complete sphere you must revolve the profile 360°.

[9] Click on *Revolve 360°* ⊙.

[10] Click on *Finish*.

Fig. 3.43

You should get a sphere like the one shown in Fig. 3.42(a).

In the profile step of a revolved protrusion you must select an axis of revolution. It must be a straight line and the remainder of the profile must be entirely on one side of that line. However, you cannot create the above sphere by drawing a circle in the profile with the axis of revolution passing through its centre and then revolving it 180°. You will get the message shown in Fig. 3.44 if you try this.

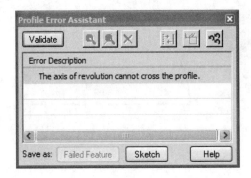

Fig. 3.44

3.5.2   Torus

Another common shape that can be constructed using the revolved protrusion is a torus, or a donut, like the one shown in Fig. 3.40. To create the partial torus shown in Fig. 3.45(a):

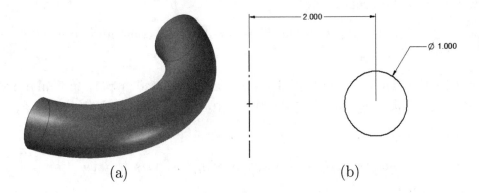

(a)   (b)

Fig. 3.45

1 Create a new part.

2 Click on *Revolved Protrusion* Revol...

3 Select the *Front* reference plane as the profile plane.

[4] Draw the profile shown in Fig. 3.45(b).

[5] Select the axis of revolution.

The profile is composed of a line, the axis of revolution, and a circle. The length of the axis of revolution does not matter.

[6] Click on *Return*.

[7] In the extent step, select *Finite Extent* .

[8] Type an angle of 150 on the ribbon bar.

By default the feature protrudes from only one direction of the profile plane, that is, a *Non-symmetric Extent* .

[9] Click on *Symmetric Extent* .

You will see that the revolved protrusion now extends 75° in both directions from the profile plane and your part should appear as shown in Fig. 3.45(a) when displayed isometrically.

3.5.3   Revolved Protrusion with Complex Profile

As a further demonstration, construct the part shown in Fig. 3.46(a). This part can be drawn using a single revolved protrusion, but try to constructed it as directed.

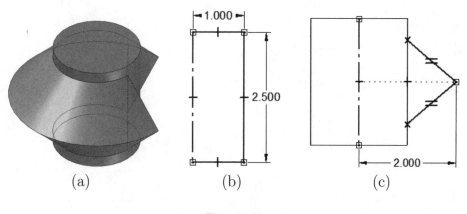

(a)   (b)   (c)

Fig. 3.46

[1] Create a new part.

[2] Click on *Revolved Protrusion* Revol...

[3] Select any reference plane as the profile plane.

[4] Draw the rectangular profile shown in Fig. 3.46(b) to get a cylinder.

[5] Select the left vertical line as the axis of revolution.

[6] Click on *Revolve 360°* .

[7] Finish the feature.

⑧ Click on *Revolved Protrusion* Revol...

⑨ Select the same profile plane as the first feature by clicking on *LastPlane* from the *Create-from Options* pull-down menu on the *Plane or Sketch Step* ribbon bar.

⑩ Draw the open profile shown in Fig. 3.46(c).

Do not worry about being exact with this profile. If your profile appears as shown in Fig. 3.47 your revolved protrusion will still work.

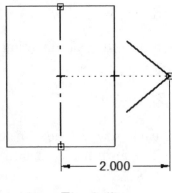

Fig. 3.47

⑪ Draw a line as the axis of revolution. Click on *Axis of Revolution* Axis of.. and then select the line.

⑫ Click on *Return*.

⑬ In *Side Step*, select the side indicated by the arrow in Fig. 3.48.

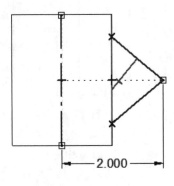

Fig. 3.48

⑭ Enter an extent *Angle* of 270.

⑮ Click on *Finish*.

You will notice that because an open profile is used in the second feature, the side step is not skipped and you must specify on which side of the open profile the solid will be.

3.6 Revolved Cutout Feature

A *Revolved Cutout* Revol.. is a feature constructed by removing the material swept by a profile along a circular arc path. It is analogous to a cutout feature using a circular sweep path. The steps are identical to that of the revolved protrusion. To add this feature, your part must have a positive volume. In addition, be warned that when creating more than one profile for the same feature, all profiles must be closed. If you are using a single profile, it does not necessarily have to be closed.

An example of a part containing a revolved cutout is shown in Fig. 3.49(a). The first feature is a simple $1 \times 2 \times 2$ block. The second feature is a revolved cutout whose profile, drawn on the bottom face of the block, is shown in Fig. 3.50. Note that the axis of revolution is the rightmost edge. The profile is open. If the two horizontal lines of the profile are omitted, then the part shown in Fig. 3.49(b) will result. If the profile is not closed, Solid Edge closes it implicity by connecting the two endpoints together with a straight line before sweeping the profile.

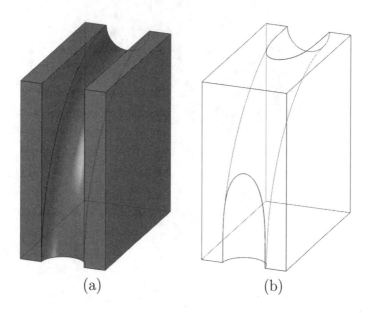

(a)   (b)

Fig. 3.49

As practice create the part shown in Fig. 3.51:

1. Create a new part.
2. Create a *Revolved Protrusion* feature.
3. Select the *Front* reference plane.
4. Draw the quarter-circle profile shown in Fig. 3.52. Use the *Arc by Center* Arcby.. command to draw the arc.
5. Select the left vertical edge as the axis of revolution.
6. Make its extent 360°.
7. Finish the feature.

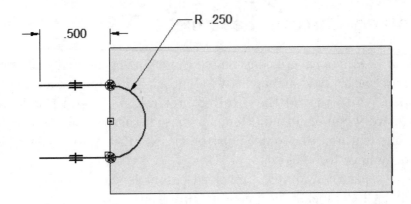

Fig. 3.50

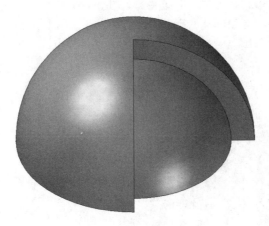

Fig. 3.51

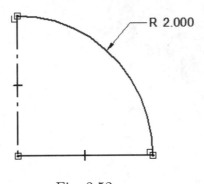

Fig. 3.52

8 Start a *Revolved Cutout* feature by clicking on Revol...

9 Select the *Front* reference plane for the profile plane.

10 Draw the open profile shown in Fig. 3.53, comprised of two lines and an arc. Use the *Arc by Center* Arc by.. command to draw the arc.

11 Draw and select the axis of revolution.

12 In *Side Step*, choose the arrow pointing up or away from the centre of the sphere.

13 Select a symmetric extent of 90°.

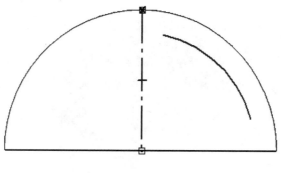

Fig. 3.53

14 | Finish the feature.

3.7   Thin Wall Feature

A *Thin Wall* Thin.. feature "hollows out" the part. Like the cutout feature, a thin wall cannot be your first feature because it subtracts volume from existing features. A thin wall feature requires you to complete the following steps, shown on the ribbon bar in Fig. 3.54.

Fig. 3.54

1. *Common Thickness* ,
2. *Open Faces* , and
3. *Unique Thickness* .

In the common thickness step, you must choose a common wall thickness for all walls of your part. In the following two steps you specify the exceptions. In the open faces step, select the faces where you wish to have a zero wall thickness — that is, the open faces will make the interior hollow open to the outside. In the last step, select the faces that you want to have a unique thickness (i.e., neither zero nor the common wall thickness). The thin wall feature applies to the entire design body up to the point the thin wall feature is applied.

As an example, try creating the part shown in Fig. 3.55.

1 | Create a new part.

2 | Create a block using a protrusion feature with the proportions $3 \times 4 \times 5$. Use the *Rectangle* Recta.. command to create the profile.

3 | Click on *Thinwall* Thin...

4 | Type *.5* into the *Common thickness* on the ribbon bar and press the *Enter* key.

5 | Select the top face and one of the vertical faces of the block shown in Fig. 3.56.

6 | Click on *Accept* on the ribbon bar.

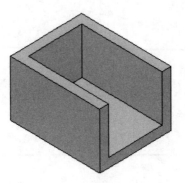

Fig. 3.55

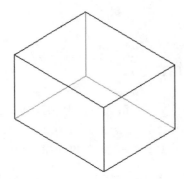

Fig. 3.56

7 Click on *Preview* on the ribbon bar.

Your model area should appear as shown in Fig. 3.57.

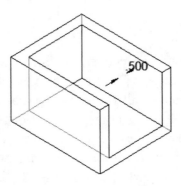

Fig. 3.57

8 Click on *Finish* on the ribbon bar.

3.8   Drawing Commands

All your profiles will be composed from a few of the most common geometric elements:

- lines,
- circles,
- circular arcs (part of a circle), and
- ellipses.

Solid Edge provides the following commands for creating these elements in profiles. All these commands appear on the *Draw Toolbar* when you edit profiles. Each command has its own ribbon bar like the one for the *Line* command shown in Fig. 3.58.

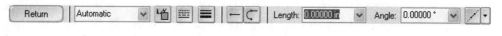

Fig. 3.58

Note the text boxes for *Length* and *Angle*. These allow you to specify initial values for these parameters. The ribbon bar for each of the following commands prompts you to enter values specific to the command. Values may be entered with or without units. If you do not enter units the default units for the current part will be assumed. If you do not enter values for these parameters Solid Edge will fill them using your mouse inputs.

- *Line* Line — Draws a chain of straight line segments and circular arcs. The first time you click in the model area a line or an arc is created. Each additional click adds another line connected to the previous one. Select the ⊟ icon and ⌒ icon on the ribbon bar (Fig. 3.58) to switch between lines and arcs, respectively. Note that the angle of the arc at its start point is determined by the direction you move your mouse pointer away from the start point.
- Three commands for creating circular arcs are available:

  – *Arc by 3 Points* Arc by.. — Draws an arc, given a start point, an endpoint, and another point on the arc.
  – *Tangent Arc* Tange.. — Draws an arc tangent or perpendicular to one or two elements.
  – *Arc by Center* Arc by.. — Draws an arc, given a centre point, a start point, and an endpoint. The direction of the arc (clockwise or counterclockwise) is determined by the direction you move your mouse pointer away from the start point.
- There are three commands for creating full circles:

  – *Circle by Center* Circle.. — Draws a circle, given a centre and specified radius.
  – *Circle by 3 Points* Circle.. — Draws an arc through any three non-coincident points.
  – *Tangent Circle* Tange.. — Draws a circle tangent to one or two elements.
- There are two commands for creating ellipses:

  – *Ellipse by 3 Points* Ellips.. — Draws an ellipse, given three points.
  – *Ellipse by Center* Ellips.. — Draws an ellipse, given a centre point and the endpoints of the two axes.

- *Rectangle* Recta.. — Draws a rectangle, given two corners and a length. Rectangles are not necessarily aligned with the *x*- or *y*-axes.

3.9   Select Tool and QuickPick Commands

The *Select Tool* Select.. cancels the current command and allows you to select planes, features, profile elements, dimensions, relationship handles, etc. Before you can manipulate, delete, or modify any of these items they must be selected first.

Occasionally, it is difficult to select an item because there are many in the same area in the current view of the design body. Solid Edge's *QuickPick* facility helps you accurately select the item you want. If you create a cube (using a single protrusion) like the one shown in Fig. 3.59(a), you would normally select a feature by clicking on it. Alternatively, hover your mouse pointer over the part. If you hold the mouse still for a few seconds, a tiny icon of a three-button mouse will appear next to your pointer. Right-click and you will get the QuickPick menu shown in Fig. 3.59(b). The menu shows you a list of items available for selection near the region of the mouse. Just move your mouse over the menu items to make your selection and click. *Design Body* refers to the entire part — all features.

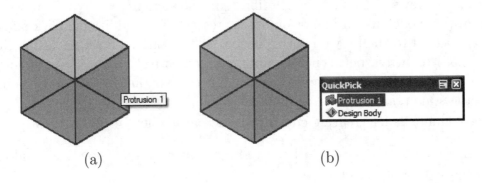

(a)   (b)

Fig. 3.59

The QuickPick facility is available wherever you make selections in the model area, including within other commands and when creating profiles. Begin the cutout command. Select a profile plane using the *Coincident Plane* option. Move your cursor to the bottom right of the cube in isometric view. Pause. Right-click to get the menu shown in Fig. 3.60(b). By moving your cursor over the menu you can select various faces in the area of the mouse pointer, as shown in Fig. 3.60(c).

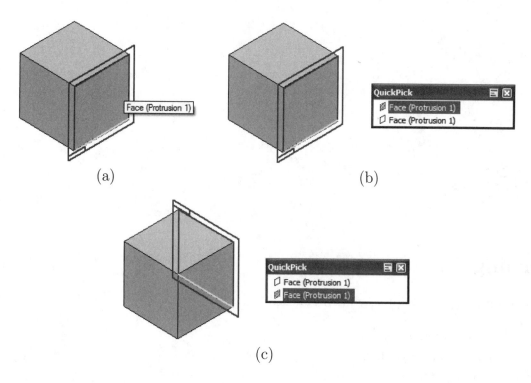

(a)

(b)

(c)

Fig. 3.60

Exercises

1. All exercises for this chapter are located at www.pearsoned.ca/text/fleisig. For each exercise, download it, read it, and create a Solid Edge part to reproduce the part in the drawing exactly. All exercises show a fully dimensioned isometric pictorial. A second isometric pictorial of the same part may be shown to aid visualization. Some isometric pictorials may contain hidden lines to show internal or hidden features. Creating a new part from scratch can be a difficult task the first time. Try the following:

   (a) Visualize the part. Sketch it if you need to see it better.
   (b) Plan the features. Use the minimum number of features possible.
   (c) Ensure you have used all the dimensions provided in the drawing.
   (d) Measure your part to verify all dimensions.
   (e) Orient your part to view it as it appears in the drawing: top, front, and side. Verify that the appearance of your part in these views is identical to the drawing. Note that Solid Edge draws tangent edges, whereas they do not appear in the drawings.
   (f) Check you units. Ensure you create your part in the units specified on the drawing.

CHAPTER 4

Profiles

Learning Objectives

After completing this chapter, you will be able to:

1. Define "degree of freedom."
2. Fully constrain a profile.
3. Create round and hole features.

In this chapter, you will be introduced to the concept of designer intent. To be able to determine if you have unambiguously provided all designer intent information for a profile, you will learn to locate unfixed degrees of freedom (DOF) and to constrain them. In addition, you will learn two frequently used features. The exercises at the end of the chapter will test your ability to read a multiview drawing with dimensions annotated with a pictorial and to construct parts using the features you have learned thus far.

4.1 Designer Intent

Designer intent is the information you, the designer, communicate to others regarding the details of a design, including expected usage, manufacture, service, testing, etc. For our purposes here, you are learning how to communicate your design intent with respect to the size, location, and shape of features of a part. In particular, we are going to concentrate on the design intent of profiles.

When creating a profile, you must ensure that the entire profile are fully specified. Suppose that your profile is a rectangle. You must explicitly specify both its width and height. If you just drew the profile in Solid Edge and then omitted specifying the height, Solid Edge would keep the value it assigned to the height when you drew the rectangle. You might not notice that you forgot to specify the height because visually it appears to be approximately correct. But it is unlikely to have the value you intended, although it may be close. This omission will lead to an error or ambiguity in the design. It is imperative that you fully and explicitly specify all dimensions of your profile; otherwise, you may be communicating an erroneous or ambiguous design.

4.1.1   Degrees of Freedom

What you want to know is how to methodically find out how many dimensions you need for a complex profile, in cases where it may be difficult to determine. To do so, we must introduce the concept of **degrees of freedom** or **DOFs**.

A DOF is a variable that the designer must specify to fully constrain a profile. For any given profile one can compute the number of DOFs. However, there is a virtually unlimited way of specifying or fixing the DOFs.

Every element in a profile (line, circle, circular arc, ellipse, etc.) has to be fully specified to ensure that your intent is correctly communicated. To unambiguously specify a line you need four parameters: x- and y-coordinates for a point, a distance, and an angle. Alternatively, two points could be given. Either way a line requires four parameters. These parameters, or variables, are called DOFs because to fully specify the location, orientation, and length of the line you must specify or fix all four DOFs. Similarly, each two-dimensional profile element has its own DOFs. These are summarized in Table 4.1.

Table 4.1

Element	DOFs	Description
Line	4	two points or a point, distance, and angle
Circle	3	a centre and a radius or diameter
Circular Arc	5	a centre, a radius, start and end angle
Ellipse	5	centre, major diameter, minor diameter, angle

Your profiles will generally be composed of more than one element from Table 4.1. Take, for example, the right-angled triangle in Fig. 4.1. Here the profile is composed of three lines. The total DOFs of the given drawing is 12: four DOFs per line. Therefore, to fully constrain this profile you, the designer, must specify or fix all 12 variables.

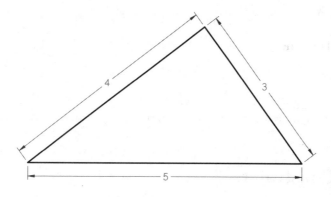

Fig. 4.1

In Solid Edge, two tools are available to you to explicitly specify design intent with respect to DOFs: dimensions and relationships. Dimensions are applied using *SmartDimension* Smart.., *Distance Between* Distan.., and with any of the commands on the *Distance Between* flyout,

Fig. 4.2. Some relationships are added automatically by Solid Edge, as you saw in the previous chapter. However, these relationships plus many others can also be added manually. See Table 4.2 for a detailed list of relationships.

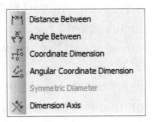

Fig. 4.2

Table 4.2

Relationship	Icon	Handle	DOFs Fixed
Connect	Connect	⊡	2
Intersect	Connect	✗	1
Concentric	Conce..	◎	2
Horizontal/Vertical	Horizo..	╪	1
Collinear	Collin..	○	1
Parallel	Parall..	//	1
Perpendicular	Perpe..	⌐	1
Lock	Lock	⌐	2
Tangent	Tangent	○	1
Equal	Equal	=	1
Symmetric	Symm..	⫮⫯	1

4.1.2   Simple Constraints

Examine the profile shown in Fig. 4.1. This is a simple 3-4-5 right-angled triangle. Let us say that you create a prism with this profile as your first feature. Your aim is to make the profile fully constrained. You begin a protrusion feature by selecting one of the three primary planes as the profile plane.

To create a fully constrained profile you will wish to generally follow these steps:

1. Choose one element (usually a line) with a known parameter (a length in the case of a line). Draw it and dimension it.
2. Place the remaining two-dimensional elements you need on the profile plane. This will include lines, arcs, circles, ellipses, etc.
3. Check that the profile is both valid and closed. Make sure all adjoining elements are connected with a connect relationship, as denoted by the handle ▣.
4. Determine how many DOFs you need to fix.
5. Add relationships and dimensions until all DOFs are fixed.
6. Check that the profile is fully constrained.

The intended profile is composed of three line segments, each carrying four DOFs for a total of 12. To fully constrain this profile you must add enough relationships and dimensions until each of these is fixed.

|1| Create a new part.

|2| Start a protrusion feature on any of the three reference planes.

|3| Draw a triangle using the *Line* line command.

Ensure that the only relationships that appear are the connect relationships (indicated by a connect relationship handle — ▣) where each of the lines touch. That is, you should see three connect relationships. If you see any other relationship handles (see Table 4.2), delete them. To delete them, hover your mouse pointer over each offending relationship handle; when it is highlighted in red, click and then press the *Delete* key. Each connect relationship ensures the endpoints of the adjacent lines are coincident. What Solid Edge is doing is adding two equations to your profile for each connect relationship. The equations might look like $x_1 = x_2$ and $y_1 = y_2$, where (x_1, y_1) and (x_2, y_2) are the respective endpoints of the adjacent lines. Consequently, each connect relationship removes two DOFs from your original twelve. That will leave you with six unfixed DOFs. Your profile should resemble Fig. 4.3.

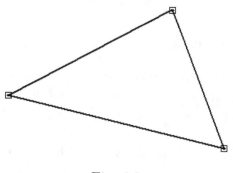

Fig. 4.3

|4| Use the *SmartDimension* tool to add the three dimensions shown in Fig. 4.1 to your profile.

You now have three unfixed DOFs remaining. See Fig. 4.4.

What DOFs remain unfixed? Clearly, the size and shape of the triangle are fully specified. However, its location and orientation in space are not.

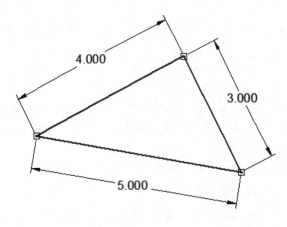

Fig. 4.4

$\boxed{5}$ Hover your mouse pointer over one of the lines.

$\boxed{6}$ Click when it is highlighted in red (Fig. 4.5).

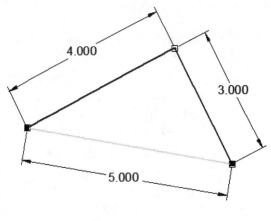

Fig. 4.5

$\boxed{7}$ Click and drag one of the endpoints of the highlighted line.

Solid Edge allows you to move only those aspects of the profile that are not constrained. The location and orientation are unconstrained; but, while dragging, the shape and size of the triangle remain fixed as specified by the relationships and dimensions you have imposed on the profile.

To fix the orientation, add a horizontal/vertical relationship to one of the lines.

$\boxed{8}$ Click on *Horizontal/Vertical* Horizo...

$\boxed{9}$ Click on one of the lines.

Try dragging again. You will see that now the orientation of the profile is fixed but its location is not. See Fig. 4.6. The horizontal/vertical relationship will snap the element you select to either the horizontal or vertical depending on which it is closer to.

To fully constrain the profile you can add a lock relationship to one of three endpoints.

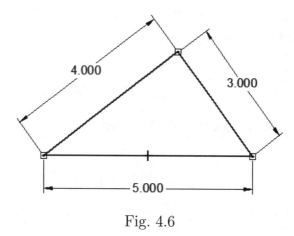

Fig. 4.6

[10] Click on *Lock* 🔒 and then click on the endpoint of one of the lines.

Try dragging again. Now the profile will not budge. Your profile should resemble Fig. 4.7.

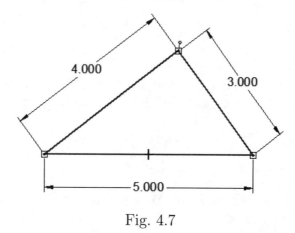

Fig. 4.7

Table 4.3 summarizes the constraints added to the triangle. It should be pointed out that for the profile of your first feature, the location and orientation are immaterial. However, for profiles of any subsequent features, location and orientation of those profiles must be fixed with respect to the design body.

The fully constrained profile shown here could be achieved by using a slightly different set of constraints.

Table 4.3

Constraint	*Count*	*DOFs Fixed*	*DOFs Remaining*
			12
Connect	3	6	6
Linear Dimension	3	3	3
Horizontal/Vertical	1	1	2
Lock	1	2	0

11	Click *Select Tool* Select...
12	Select the length 5 dimension.
13	Delete it by pressing the *Delete* key.
14	Select the length 5 line.
15	Drag one of its endpoints until it looks like Fig. 4.8.

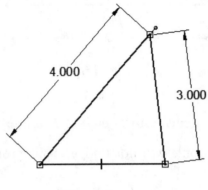

Fig. 4.8

You will see that the length of the line changes and the angles change. You have removed one dimension so now you have one unfixed DOF. Fix it by adding a perpendicular relationship.

| 16 | Click on *Perpendicular* Perpe... |
| 17 | Select the length 3 and then the length 4 lines in sequence. |

Your profile should now look like Fig. 4.9. Your profile is fully constrained once again but using a different set of constraints.

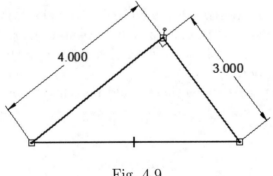

Fig. 4.9

Complete the protrusion.

18	Click on *Return*.
19	Select an extent distance.
20	Click on *Finish*.

When you are constraining profiles you are solving a set of equations. The variables are your DOFs and the equations are the relationships and dimensions you add to the profile. To have a fully constrained profile, the number of DOFs must be equal to the number of equations. Some constraints add more than one equation (i.e., connect). When you create your initial profile, how does Solid Edge decide what value the DOFs (variables) should have before you add the equations? It gets you to visually specify initial values for the elements by how you initially size, locate, and orient the various elements on the plane. As you add the equations (relationships and dimensions) Solid Edge modifies the values of the DOFs to conform to the new equations. So why not skip the constraints and specify the DOF values manually (i.e., endpoint coordinates, radii, centre coordinates, etc.)? The answer is simply that this would be extremely tedious because in some cases, as you will see in the next example, the math would be very time consuming.

4.1.3 Tangent Relationship

As another example, examine the profile in Fig. 4.10. It is obvious that it has four lines and a circular arc. Each 2D element has been given a letter label "A" through "E." According to Table 4.2 it has 21 DOFs. For argument's sake, let us ignore the orientation and location of the profile. That means you must fix 18 DOFs. To conform to Solid Edge's requirement of a connect relationship between all adjoining elements, this profile must have five connect relationships. Since each reduces the number of DOFs by two we have eight unfixed DOFs remaining. Adding five dimensions reduces this number to three. One more is accounted for by the right-angle between the horizontal and vertical lines. Notice that in engineering drawings undimensioned angles are assumed to be right angles or tangents (180°).

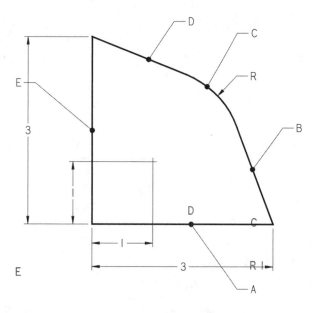

Fig. 4.10

Where are the two unfixed DOFs? They are fixed by adding tangent relationships between the arc and adjacent lines. The tangents in this profile help to fix the lengths of lines B and

D and the start and end angle of the circular arc. Without the tangents, the lengths of these lines are arbitrary as long as the other constraints are not violated.

Begin by creating element A in Fig. 4.10.

1. Create a new part.
2. Start a protrusion feature on any of the three reference planes.
3. Right-click in the model area and select *Hide All→Reference Planes*.
4. Click on *Line* Line.
5. Click in the model area.
6. Move your mouse pointer (now appearing as cross-hairs) until you see the horizontal indicator ▬ next to your mouse pointer.

This indicator means that Solid Edge will automatically give you a horizontal/vertical relationship if you click here. Your model area should appear as shown in Fig. 4.11.

Fig. 4.11

7. Click.
8. Click when your next line resembles element B in Fig. 4.10.

Make sure you do not get a vertical indicator (⌶). This line is not going to be vertical so you do not want a horizontal/vertical relationship attached to it. Your profile will resemble Fig. 4.12.

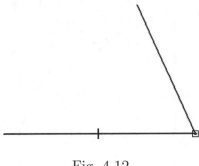

Fig. 4.12

Add the arc C.

9. Click on *Arc* ⌒ in the ribbon bar.
10. Click when the arc looks like element C in Fig. 4.12.

When you see the ⊕ shown in Fig. 4.13, Solid Edge may automatically add a tangent relationship between the arc and the adjacent line depending on the direction you take your pointer. You will need the tangent relationship, but if it is not added automatically, do not despair; you can add it later manually. Drawing arcs is notoriously difficult using this command. If it is causing difficulty try one of the other three circular arc commands:

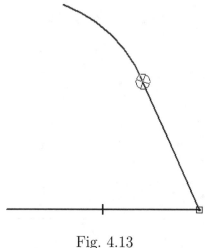

Fig. 4.13

- *Tangent Arc* Tange..,
- *Arc by 3 Points*, Arcby .., or
- *Arc by Center* Arcby ..

residing on the draw toolbar. Remember that you can add the tangent relationships (Tangent) later, but make sure that you have the required connect relationship (Connect) between the arc and adjacent line. To add a relationship, select its icon and then select the two elements you want in the relationship.

[11] Click to add the next line, D.

You may see two new indicators like those in Fig. 4.14. The dashed line on the left is the *Alignment Indicator*. It can be toggled using *Tools→Alignment Indicator* from the menu bar. In this case, it shows that if you click at that point, the endpoint of your line will be aligned vertically with the point at the opposite end of the dashed line. It ensures that when you close your profile the last line will automatically be vertical and a horizontal/vertical relationship will be applied automatically by Solid Edge. The other indicator in the top right shows that if you click there you will get a tangent relationship automatically between the line you are creating and the preceding arc. These are useful to help you complete your profile quickly, but you can always add the missing relationships manually.

[12] Complete the profile by clicking to form line E.

[13] If necessary, add any missing relationships until your profile resembles Fig. 4.15.

At this point you have a closed profile that has all the correct elements but is not fully constrained. From Fig. 4.15 you can see that the shape is not exactly right. You are still missing dimensions.

Add the dimensions shown in Fig. 4.10.

[14] Click on *SmartDimension* Smart...

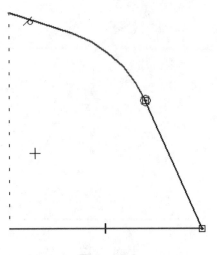

Fig. 4.14

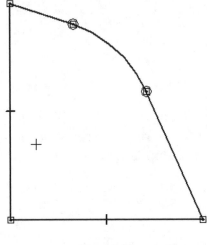

Fig. 4.15

15 Select line A.

16 Click to locate the dimension.

17 Type *3* and press *Enter*.

18 Repeat for line E and arc C.

19 Click A.

20 Click C.

21 Type *1* and press *Enter*.

22 Click to locate the dimension next to E.

23 Repeat this procedure to add a length 1 dimension between C and E.

At this point you should have two DOFs unfixed, allowing the profile to translate but not rotate in the profile plane. Verify this with the relationship assistant.

24 Click on *Tools→Dimensions→Relationship Assistant* from the menu bar. You will get the ribbon bar shown in Fig. 4.16.

25 Click on any of the elements of your profile to select it.

26 Click on *Show Variability*  in the ribbon bar.

Fig. 4.16

The number next to *Relationships needed* in the ribbon bar indicates the number of remaining unfixed DOFs. You should see two here because there are only two unfixed DOFs: for translation in the x and y directions. In addition, look in the model area. You will see a red outline of your profile.

27 Click on *Show Variability* repeatedly.

Clicking repeatedly will animate the profile. In this way, Solid Edge demonstrates possible solutions to the set of dimensions and relationships you specified for the profile. This is a very useful way of telling if your profile is fully constrained and where additional dimensions and relationships might be necessary.

28 Add a *Lock* relationship at an endpoint to fully constrain your profile.

Complete the protrusion.

29 Click on *Return*.

30 Select an extent distance.

31 Click on *Finish*.

Your finished and fully constrained profile will look like Fig. 4.17.

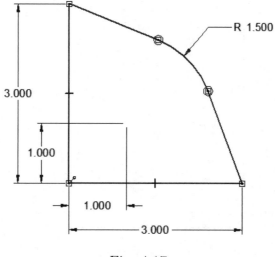

Fig. 4.17

4.1.4   Solving for a Set of Dimensions and Relationships

Unfortunately, using constraints can lead to problems because sometimes there is more than one correct solution. Consider Fig. 4.18(a). This is a closed profile drawn according to Fig. 4.10. However, when a tangent relationship is added, Fig. 4.18(b) results. This is because the adjoining line and arc can be tangent to each other in one of two ways, as shown in Fig. 4.10 or in Fig. 4.18(a). Solid Edge will choose the solution that the current profile is closest to. Therefore, to avoid this problem, you must ensure that the profile looks more like Fig. 4.10 before you add the tangent relationship.

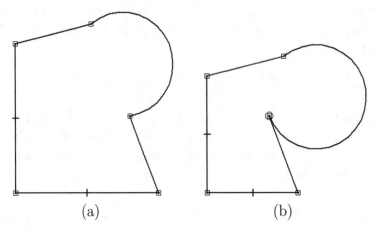

(a)   (b)

Fig. 4.18

To adjust this you must click on *Select Tool* Select.. and then click on the arc. Your profile will appear as shown in Fig. 4.19. Now by dragging one of the four key points of the arc, marked by filled screen squares, you can adjust the shape of the arc to look more like it is intended and then add the tangent relationship once more.

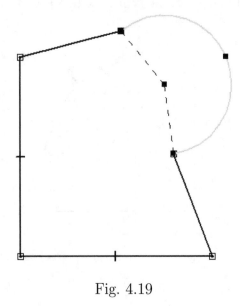

Fig. 4.19

By dragging the centre of the arc, Fig. 4.20(a) was obtained. The tangent relationship was added by first clicking on the line and then the arc to produce Fig. 4.20(b). Clicking first on the arc and then on the line produces Fig. 4.20(c). When adding a relationship to a profile requiring two elements, the second element you click will remain stationary or fixed and the first will be moved unless other constraints make that impossible.

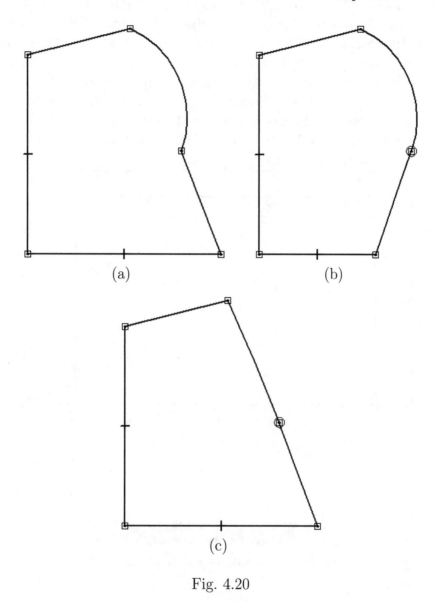

(a)

(b)

(c)

Fig. 4.20

Adjusting the profile shape manually produces a better solution in Fig. 4.20(b) or Fig. 4.20(c) than in Fig. 4.18(b). In general, if adding a dimension or relationship produces unexpected results, click *Edit→Undo* and do one of two things:

1. proceed by adding the relationships and dimensions in another order; or
2. modify the shape of the profile manually to more closely resemble your intend profile.

4.1.5 Redundant Constraints and Not To Scale Dimensions

The relationship assistant is used to determine if a profile is underconstrained. No similar tool exists to determine if a profile is overconstrained. Solid Edge will allow you to overconstrain a profile, as shown in Fig. 4.21. A rectangle has 16 DOFs. The profile shown has four connect relationships, four horizontal/vertical relationships, four perpendicular relationships, and four dimensions. In total, these constraints could fix 20 DOFs. Solid Edge will permit you to add as many redundant relationships as you wish as long as they do not conflict. Clearly, the perpendicular and horizontal/vertical relationships perform the same function for this profile. Removing either would not change the profile and would not underconstrain it. However, if you attempted to add a perpendicular relationship to parallel lines you would get the response shown in Fig. 4.22 and your attempt would be ignored by Solid Edge.

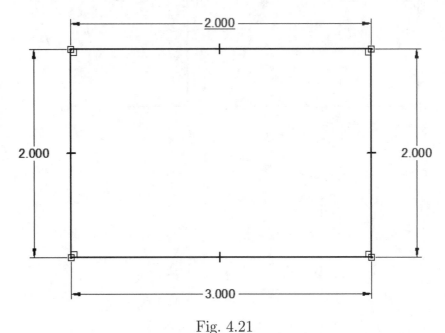

Fig. 4.21

Fig. 4.22

Redundant dimensions are flagged by colour. Normal non-redundant dimensions are coloured black, but when you add a dimension for a DOF that is already fixed Solid Edge will colour the dimension blue. This will occur if you are duplicating an existing dimension or if the DOF you wish to fix with the dimension is already fixed by other constraints. For example, consider the right-angled triangle of Fig. 4.1. If the length 5 dimension is removed and a perpendicular relationship is added between the lines of length 3 and 4, the triangle would still be fully constrained. The dimensions (in black) of length 3 and 4 are considered **driving dimensions**. That is because you can click on the dimension and change the value. Solid Edge will not modify this dimension under any circumstances. If you now added a dimension to the length 5 side (without removing the perpendicular relationship), you clearly have an overconstrained profile. The value of the length 5 dimension is determined by the other relationships and dimensions already present on the profile. Consequently, Solid Edge colours this dimension blue. A blue dimension is called a **driven dimension** because its value is determined by other constraints and the designer cannot modify it.

You can try to modify a driven dimension by selecting it and typing a new value in the ribbon bar. However, your dimension value will not reflect the actual value of the associated DOF. Observe that in Fig. 4.21 the horizontal length 2 dimension is underlined. This means the dimension is **not to scale**. In other words, this is warning that the dimension value displayed does not reflect the actual value.

The value of driven dimensions cannot be modified but the value of driving dimensions can. You may have noticed that there is another way to modify a key dimension. Instead of adding a dimension, just click on a line and modify its length in the ribbon bar. There is a real danger in modifying the lengths of elements in this manner. This value is an **initial value**. This means that Solid Edge may modify it when new constraints are added to the profile. For example, try to create a profile of an equilateral triangle. Ensure it is a closed profile with no constraints other than three connect relationships. In turn, modify the lengths of each of the three lines by selecting them and then entering the same length for all three sides. You will notice that when you are done it is not an equilateral triangle. Solid Edge has modified the length of one of the sides in response to your length modifications. This underscores the fact that these initial values are only that and to ensure that these values do not change you must apply dimensions. You must use the *Equal* Equal relationship or the SmartDimension tool to ensure all sides are equal.

In summary, always add a constraint, i.e., a dimension or relationship, to fix a DOF. Modifying an initial value will likely result in an incorrect profile because, when modifying the profile, Solid Edge will attempt to solve the given set of equations by modifying initial values.

4.1.6   IntelliSketch

Solid Edge's *IntelliSketch* is a set of tools that help you make sketches more precisely and quickly. You have already been introduced to a number of the capabilities of IntelliSketch. This section will serve to remind you of some of the tools you have learned and introduce a few new ones.

Ostensibly, you could design each new profile by placing the elements you need on the page and then adding all the relationships you needed manually. IntelliSketch helps you by suggesting relationships as you draw. When IntelliSketch suggests a relationship you will see one or two indicators next to your mouse pointer (Fig. 4.23). See Table 4.4 for a list of common relationships and their indicators. From the menu bar *Tools→IntelliSketch→Relationships* you can choose which relationships can be suggested by Solid Edge.

As you move your mouse pointer you will notice that the relationship indicators appear

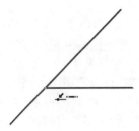

Fig. 4.23

within a small area. To control the size of this area, click on *Tools→IntelliSketch→Cursor* in the menu bar (Fig. 4.24(b)).

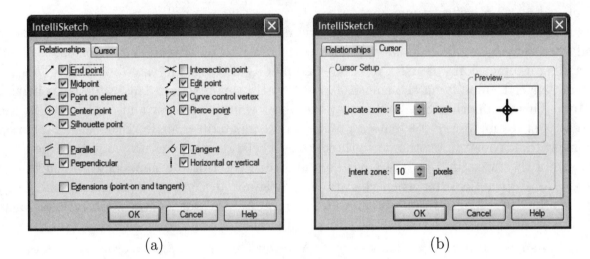

(a)   (b)

Fig. 4.24

Table 4.4

Name	Indicator
Intersect	✕
Endpoint	╱
Midpoint	─•─
Centre Point	⊕
Point on Element	⬦
Horizontal or Vertical	▃ or ┊
Parallel	⫽
Perpendicular	⌐
Tangent	↗
Silhouette	⌒
Pierce Point	⋈

The alignment indicators are an IntelliSketch feature with which you are familiar. Use alignment indicators to horizontally or vertically align key points on elements. In Fig. 4.25, the centre of the rectangle is located by extending the alignment indicators from two mid-points.

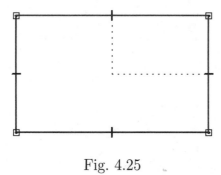

Fig. 4.25

Finding the centre of an arc or a circle requires you to hover your mouse pointer over the arc first. Then the centre of the arc will appear as shown in Fig. 4.26. Otherwise you cannot select the centre of an arc.

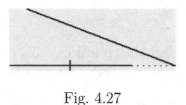

Fig. 4.26

IntelliSketch recognizes points on arcs and lines as if those elements were infinite. See Fig. 4.27.

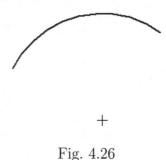

Fig. 4.27

4.1.7 Construction Elements

Sometimes it is useful to be able to have elements in your profile that help you locate and shape the profile but are not part of the profile. These are called construction elements. You can easily turn any element in a profile into a construction element with the *Construction* Constr.. command. Fig. 4.28 shows an example of the use of a construction element. The horizontal line has been selected as a construction element. Notice the line type. The relationship assistant will count unfixed DOFs from construction elements. They must be fully constrained like any other part of the profile.

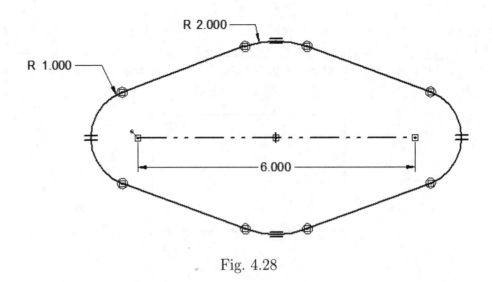

Fig. 4.28

4.2   Include

When you are creating a profile based on an existing feature and you wish to incorporate parts of previous features in your current profile, the *Include* ⌘ command will aid you. Create the part in Fig. 4.29(a).

1   Create a new part.

2   Begin a protrusion feature.

3   Select the *Front* reference plane as the profile plane.

4   Create the profile in Fig. 4.29(b). Your profile will resemble Fig. 4.30.

5   Give the protrusion an extent of *1* unit.

6   Begin a second protrusion feature.

7   Select the face bounded by the profile in Fig. 4.29(b) as the profile plane.

8   Click on *Include* Include.

9   When you see the dialogue box shown in Fig. 4.31, click *OK*.

10 Select the edges labelled A, B, F, and G, in Fig. 4.29(b).

11 Using the *Line* Line command, complete the profile as shown in Fig. 4.32.

12 Set the extent to *1* unit.

13 Measure the physical properties *Inspect→Physical Properties* and compare them with Table 4.5.

Note the chain link indicator on the included elements in Fig. 4.32. This indicates an associative relationship between these two elements in the current profile and their source in the previous feature.

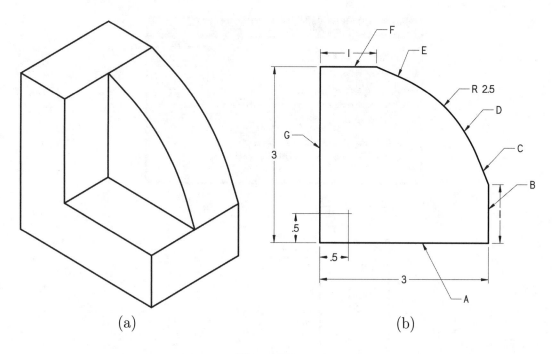

(a)   (b)

Fig. 4.29

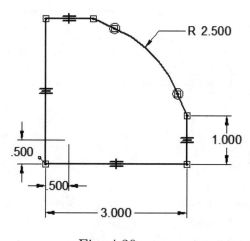

Fig. 4.30

Table 4.5

Volume		12.691 unit^3
Surface Area		38.336 unit^2
	K1	1.1982 unit
Radii of Gyration	K2	1.1020 unit
	K3	0.89244 unit

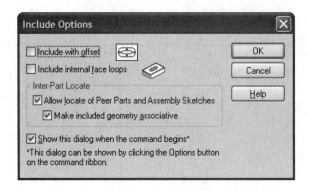

Fig. 4.31

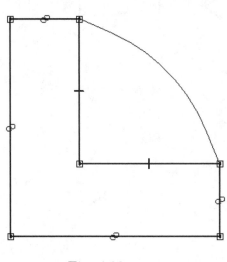

Fig. 4.32

4.3   Round Feature

The *Round* ![Round] feature, appearing on the feature toolbar, rounds the edges of parts. One edge of the cube shown in Fig. 4.33(a) is rounded to give Fig. 4.33(b). This is an example of an outside round. One edge of the L-shaped part shown in Fig. 4.33(c) is rounded to give Fig. 4.33(d). This is an example of an inside round or fillet.

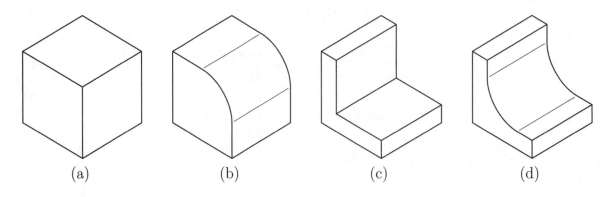

Fig. 4.33

When you select the round command, your ribbon bar will appear as shown in Fig. 4.34. Here you see that the command has three steps:

Fig. 4.34

1. *Select Step* ,
2. *Round Parameters* , and
3. *Soften Corner Step* .

In its simplest form, taught here, you will only apply a constant radius round. In this case, the steps can be reduced to the following:

1. Select the edges to be rounded.
2. Input a radius on the ribbon bar.
3. Click on *Preview* on the ribbon bar.
4. Click on *Finish* on the ribbon bar.

Do the following example.

1. Create a new part.
2. Create a protrusion with a one-unit square profile.
3. Give the protrusion a one-unit extent.
4. Start the thin wall feature.
5. Select a wall thickness of $\frac{1}{4}$. Your part should resemble Fig. 4.35.

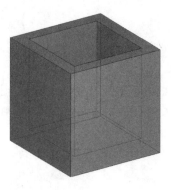

Fig. 4.35

6. Click on *Round* Round.
7. Select all the edges.
8. Type a radius of $\frac{1}{8}$.

Your part should resemble Fig. 4.36.

Fig. 4.36

4.4 Hole Feature

The *Hole* ⬚ feature is a simple way of creating specialized round holes, including: simple, threaded, tapered, counterbore, countersunk, blind, through, etc. Although it is true that you can create all these features except the thread using the cutout and revolved cutout features, the hole feature is easier and quicker to use.

The hole feature involves three steps plus options shown in the ribbon bar in Fig. 4.37. The steps are:

1. *Plane Step* 🔲,
2. *Hole Step* ⬦, and
3. *Extent Step* 🔲.

In addition, the *Hole Options* are set by clicking on the 🔲 icon on the ribbon bar.

Fig. 4.37

When starting a hole feature, click on *Hole Options* 🔲 first. You will see a dialogue box like the one shown in Fig. 4.38(a). The options here allow you to select the type of hole under *Type* and the various parameters associated with each. The hole types are:

1. simple,
2. threaded,
3. tapered,
4. counterbore, and
5. countersink.

The simple type can easily be duplicated by a cutout or revolved cutout feature. The threaded type (Fig. 4.38(b)) is a simple hole with a thread. The tapered hole (Fig. 4.39(a)) is a simple hole with constantly varying hole diameter (a cone-shaped hole). A counterbore hole (Fig. 4.39(b)) has a larger diameter at the opening and a countersunk hole (Fig. 4.39(c)) has a conical or bevelled opening. The options vary for each of the hole types. However, on

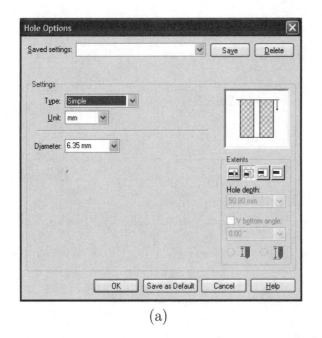

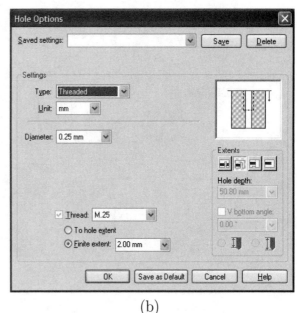

(a)   (b)

Fig. 4.38

the right side of the dialogue box is a diagram of the hole based on the current parameters. The counterbore and countersink hole types can also be threaded. The options directly before the *Type* pull-down box are self-explanatory. Buttons located below the diagram on the right of the dialogue box allow you to select the *Extents* of the hole. These options are similar to those of the protrusion and cutout features:

1. *Through All* ⊟,
2. *Through Next* ⊟,
3. *From/To Extent* ⊟, and
4. *Finite Extent* ⊟.

Once the hole type, parameters, and extents are selected, go to selecting the profile plane in the plane step. This step is identical to the step of the same name in protrusion features. The following step, the hole step, differs in one significant way from the other profile step you are familiar with. There is only one type of 2D element that you can place on the profile: a *Hole Circle* Hole C., which is found on the *Features and Relationships* toolbar. The usual 2D elements such as line and circle by centre are still found on the draw toolbar. However, if you place them on your profile in a hole feature they will be treated as construction geometry. The hole circle is how you locate one or more holes. Once placed, clicking *Return* will take you to the extent step. Here you select the direction that the hole will extend from the profile plane in the same manner you would choose the extent direction for a protrusion or cutout.

For practice, try creating the part shown in the multiview in Fig. 4.40(a). This part requires no more than three features.

1 Create a new part with default units of millimetres.

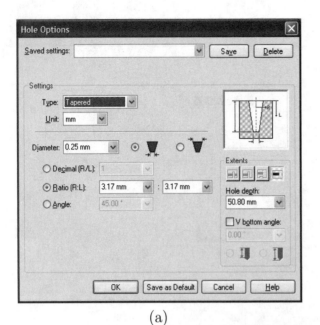

(a)

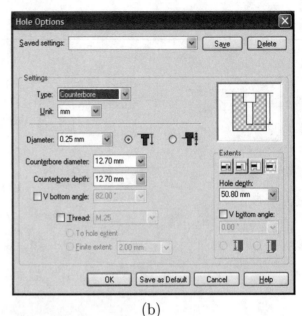

(b)

(c)

Fig. 4.39

2 Create a protrusion for the first feature using the front view in Fig. 4.40(a) as your profile.

3 Start the *Hole* Hole command.

4 Select the one of the faces on which the countersunk holes are located as the profile plane.

5 Click on *Hole Circle* Hole C...

6 Place two hole circles.

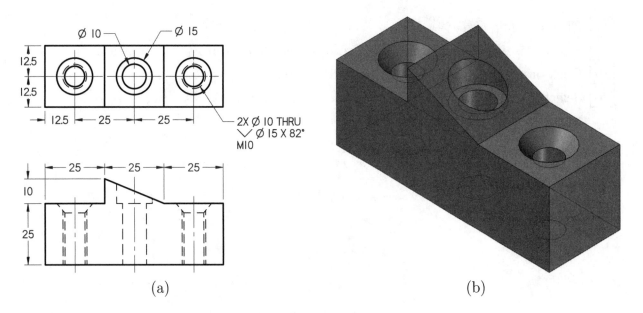

Fig. 4.40

7 Use SmartDimension to fully constrain their locations.

8 Click on *Return*.

9 Click in the model area to select the direction of the hole.

10 Click on *Hole Options* 🔳▾.

11 Select the *Countersink* hole type.

12 Set 10 as the hole diameter, 15 for the countersink diameter, 82.00° as the countersink angle, and M10 as the thread.

13 Select *To hole extent*.

14 Set the hole extent to be *Through Next*.

15 Click on *OK*.

16 Click on *Finish*.

Notice when you complete this feature that the hole is green where the thread ought to appear. Solid Edge does not render the threads realistically but instead uses the colour green to schematically indicate a threaded surface. The developers of Solid Edge chose to trade off realistic threads for greater rendering speed. A realistic thread has many faces and thus would add considerable additional computation time to rendering.

Now add the last feature, a counterbore hole (without thread). From the multiview you will see that the bottom of the counterbore is in line with the top horizontal surface of the part.

17 Click on *Hole Circle* Hole C.. .

18 Select *Parallel Plane* ⬠ from the *Create-From Options* drop-down menu box.

19 Click on the face on which you placed the first two holes.

20 Select a keypoint at the top of the part (top of the peak). See Fig. 4.41.

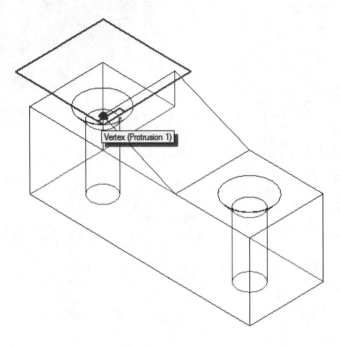

Fig. 4.41

21 Locate and constrain the hole circle.

22 Click on *Return*.

23 Click in the model area to select the direction of the hole.

24 Click on *Hole Options* ⊞▾.

25 Set the counterbore parameters: diameter to 10, counterbore diameter to 15, and counterbore depth to 10.

26 Select *To hole extent*.

27 Set the hole extent to *Through Next*.

28 Click on *OK*.

29 Click on *Finish*.

Your part should now resemble Fig. 4.40(b).

Exercises

1. All exercises for this chapter are located at www.pearsoned.ca/text/fleisig. For each exercise, download it, read it, and create a Solid Edge part to reproduce the part in the drawing exactly. All exercises show one fully dimensioned multiview projection of a part. An isometric pictorial of the same part aids visualization. Some isometric pictorials may contain hidden lines to show internal or hidden features. When creating complex profiles consider the following:

    (a) Always fully constrain your profile. Use the Relationship Assistant to verify profiles are fully constrained.

    (b) Do not construct a part from multiple Protrusion or Revolved Protrusion features if only one will suffice just to avoid a more complex profile. This will lead to errors and makes corrections to parts difficult.

    (c) If you can use a Round feature then use it and avoid adding it to a round or a fillet to a profile.

CHAPTER 5

Part Editing

Learning Objectives

After completing this chapter, you will be able to:

1. Edit feature steps.
2. Edit features.

Your knowledge of features and steps used will be furthered with the understanding of how to modify features without deleting and creating them. The exercises at the end of the chapter will test your ability to read a dimensioned multiview and create parts using the features you have learned thus far.

Solid modelling software in general captures not only the final shape of the part you are designing but also retains the steps you have taken to construct the part. These steps include each feature and individual operations, selections, and parameters you have made for each feature. Consequently, you do not have to start over if you want to change something in an earlier feature or a step within a feature.

The design model displayed in the model area is the sum total of the features presented in the Feature Pathfinder. In other words, to construct the design model, Solid Edge computes each feature in sequence. A change to any feature means that Solid Edge must recompute that feature and its descendants to get the changed design model.

5.1 Feature Step Editing

Solid Edge provides for three ways of editing features without having to delete and recreate them. They are:

1. *Edit Definition* ⬚,
2. *Edit Profile* ⬚, and
3. *Dynamic Edit* ⬚.

To perform one of these three actions, first select a feature either by clicking on it in the Feature Pathfinder or by clicking on the feature in the model area. A selected feature will be outlined in yellow. Then select one of the three feature edit commands either from the

ribbon bar (Fig. 5.1) or you can right-click the feature in the Feature Pathfinder and select
the command from the context menu (see Fig. 5.2).

Fig. 5.1

Fig. 5.2

5.1.1   Dynamic Edit

The *Dynamic Edit* ⌨ command shows you the dimensions of the feature in the model area
as shown for the simple protrusion in Fig. 5.3. Any dimensions placed on a profile will
appear when using Dynamic Edit as well as parameters such as protrusion depth. To modify
a dimension, click on it and change its value in the ribbon bar.

5.1.2   Edit Profile

The *Edit Profile* ⌨ command takes you directly to the profile step of a feature, if the feature
contains a profile. All the commands you have available during the initial creation of the
profile are also available when editing it.

5.1.3   Edit Definition

Use the *Edit Definition* ⌨ command to modify any step or parameter of any given feature.
Once you have selected the feature and clicked the edit definition command, the SmartStep

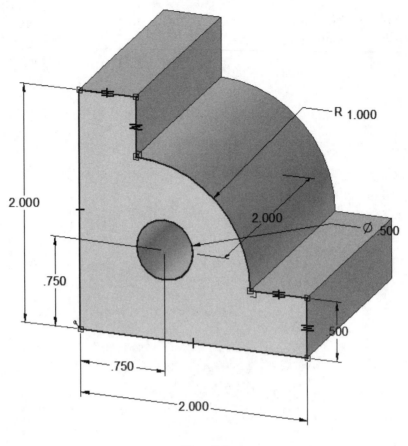

Fig. 5.3

ribbon bar specific to the type of feature you have selected will appear. The ribbon bar for a protrusion feature is shown in Fig. 5.4(a), for example. In general, the left side of the ribbon bar (to the left of the vertical bar) will display icons representing the individual steps you followed to construct the feature. The item to the right of the vertical bar, in this case the *Name*, displays options and selections specific to the current step. When no step is selected, as it is initially, then you can modify the name of the feature. Normally when you are constructing a feature, Solid Edge will automatically move forward through the step for you. When editing a feature, you select the step you want to modify and then make the necessary choices to complete that step. The SmartStep ribbon bar means that you do not have to restart a feature to make changes. To exit the edit definition command select the *Select Tool* Select.. command. The ribbon bar for the same feature is shown at the *Treatment Step* in Fig. 5.4(b).

(a)   (b)

Fig. 5.4

5.2　Feature Editing

When modifying features using the above commands, previous features may be damaged because Solid Edge maintains parent/child relationships between features. Consider the part shown in Fig. 5.5(a). The contents of the Feature Pathfinder for this part are shown in Fig. 5.5(b).

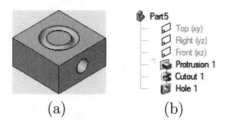

(a)　　　　　　　　　　　　(b)

Fig. 5.5

1. Create a new part.
2. Start a protrusion.
3. Select the *Front* reference plane for the profile.
4. Draw the profile shown in Fig. 5.6.

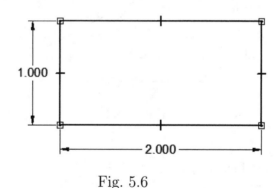

Fig. 5.6

5. Give the protrusion a depth of 2 units.
6. Start a revolved cutout.
7. Select the profile plane to be parallel to the protrusion's profile and passing through the midpoint of its depth.
8. Draw the profile shown in Fig. 5.7(a).
9. Use an extent of 360°.
10. Create a hole feature as shown in Fig. 5.5(a) with a diameter of a half. Centre the hole on the face using horizontal/vertical relationships between the centre of the circle and midpoints of the edges as shown in Fig. 5.7(b). The hole is through.

A parent/child relationship is created each time you select a feature such as an edge or face from an existing feature to create a new one. When *Protrusion 1* was created, the

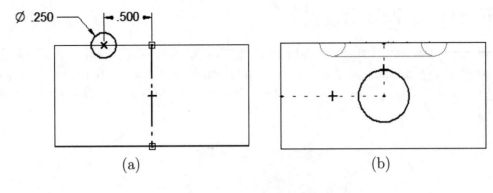

Fig. 5.7

Front plane was selected. Here the *Front* reference plane is the parent and the child is the *Protrusion 1* feature. When *Hole 1* was created, a face of *Protrusion 1* was selected. When *Cutout 1* was created, a face of *Protrusion 1* was also selected. If the parent in the relationship is modified or deleted there will be an effect on the child feature.

Consider a change in the profile of the *Protrusion 1* feature. The rectangular profile in Fig. 5.6 is modified to become the triangle in Fig. 5.8.

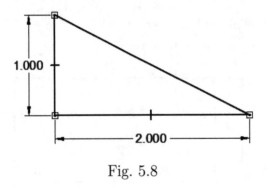

Fig. 5.8

11 Select the *Protrusion 1* feature.

12 Click on *Edit Profile* ⬚.

13 Delete two lines such that the profile now resembles Fig. 5.9.

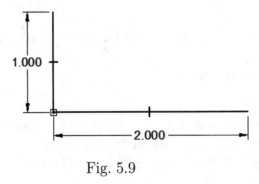

Fig. 5.9

14 Add a line to create the triangle shown in Fig. 5.8.

[15] Click on *Return.*

[16] Click on *Finish.*

The result is the part shown in Fig. 5.10(a) with the Feature Pathfinder appearing as shown in Fig. 5.10(b).

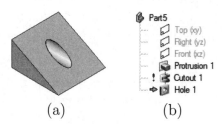

(a)   (b)

Fig. 5.10

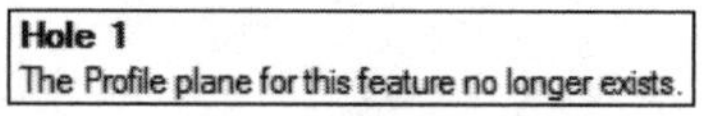

Hole 1
The Profile plane for this feature no longer exists.

Fig. 5.11

The arrow next to *Hole 1* indicates that there is a problem with the feature. If you hover your mouse pointer over the *Hole 1* feature in the Feature Pathfinder, Solid Edge will issue the message in Fig. 5.11. This means that the face you selected as your profile plane for the *Hole 1* feature was deleted. That face is the protrusion of the right edge of the profile in Fig. 5.6, which you deleted. Since that parent/child relationship is broken, Solid Edge has still computed the hole but has used the location and position of a face that no longer exists. To eliminate the warning you must correct the error.

[17] Select the *Hole 1* feature.

[18] Click on *Edit Definition* 🔲.

[19] Click on *Plane Step* 🔲.

[20] Select the slanted face.

However, this does not fix the entire problem. The arrow remains but a new warning is shown, as in Fig. 5.12. Now edit the profile of the hole feature.

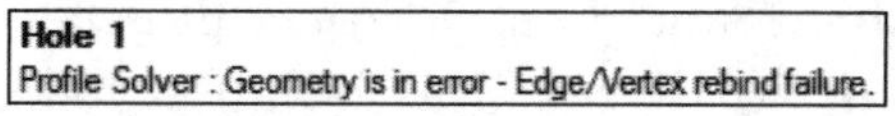

Hole 1
Profile Solver : Geometry is in error - Edge/Vertex rebind failure.

Fig. 5.12

[21] Click on *Hole Step* 🔲.

The profile should appear brown, denoting that some relationships are linked to elements that no longer exist.

22 Delete the horizontal/vertical relationships you added earlier to link the centre of the circle to the edges of *Protrusion 1*.

23 Click on *Return*.

24 Click on *Finish*.

Your profile will return to its normal colour.

The revolved cutout feature, *Cutout 1*, has a red exclamation mark next to it because the edges selected for inclusion in the round feature no longer exist. Solid Edge indicates this with the message in Fig. 5.13.

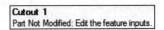

Fig. 5.13

A different way of modifying the rectangular profile of Fig. 5.6 into the triangle of Fig. 5.8 will yield different results.

25 Click the *Edit→Undo* and/or *Edit→Redo* commands on the menu bar repeatedly until the part looks like Fig. 5.5(a).

26 Edit the profile of *Protrusion 1*.

27 Delete the top horizontal edge and the horizontal/vertical relationship on the right edge. See Fig. 5.14.

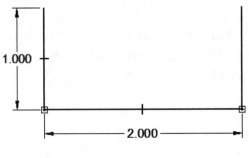

Fig. 5.14

28 Add a connect relationship to close the profile and form the triangle (Fig. 5.8).

The difference is that you did not delete the right edge that forms the basis of the parent/child relationship between *Protrusion 1* and *Hole 1*. You will get the part shown in Fig. 5.15(a). This part differs from the part in Fig. 5.10(a) because you did not delete the edge that protrudes into the face that is the profile plane of the hole feature. Consequently, the profile plane of the hole is the slanted face.

5.2.1   Other Editing Commands

Features in the Feature Pathfinder can be treated by many of the same operations you are used to using in a word processor. First select one or more features. Use the *Ctrl* and/or

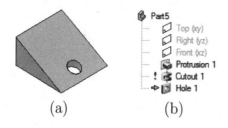

Fig. 5.15

Shift keys when clicking to select multiple features. Then right-click on one of the selected features to get the menu shown in Fig. 5.2. From here you delete, rename, cut, copy, and paste features. The other commands on this menu merit further explanation.

The *Suppress* command removes the selected features from the computed outcome of the feature list. Effectively, Solid Edge acts as if the feature is not there when it is suppressed but still retains it in the Feature Pathfinder. This can be very useful when you wish to simplify your part or edit an earlier feature without the clutter of the later features. Use *Unsuppress* on one or more features to force Solid Edge to add them back to your part model.

Similarly, the *GoTo* command suppresses all features following the currently selected one. This allows you to "insert" a feature earlier in the feature list. The *Show/Hide/Show Only* commands are intended to show/hide the entire part. Even if you select a single feature the entire part will be hidden. You will generally not find these three commands useful.

When the *Show Parents & Children Command* is applied to a feature, its parent features are marked in red and its child features in blue in the Feature Pathfinder.

Exercises

1. All exercises for this chapter are located at `www.pearsoned.ca/text/fleisig`. For each exercise, download it, read it, and create a Solid Edge part to reproduce the part in the drawing exactly. All exercises show one fully dimensioned multiview projection of a part.

CHAPTER 6

Advanced Features

Learning Objectives

After completing this chapter, you will be able to:

1. Create rib, thread, and chamfer features.
2. Duplicate features using the mirror copy feature and pattern.
3. Create sketches and reference planes.

The exercises at the end of the chapter will test your ability to read a dimensioned multiview and create parts using the Solid Edge features you have learned thus far. The drawings may contain auxiliary and section views.

6.1 Rib

A **rib** is a thin or flat feature that acts as a support. It is common in plastic parts fabricated by injection moulding. Solid Edge's *Rib* ᴿⁱᵇ command, located on the main Feature toolbar, creates a rib on a part using steps very similar to a protrusion feature. From the rib ribbon bar in Fig. 6.1, the steps are:

1. *Plane or Sketch Step* ,
2. *Draw Profile Step* ,
3. *Direction Step* , and
4. *Side Step* .

Fig. 6.1

To illustrate the subtleties of the rib command and where it deviates from the protrusion command consider the part shown in Fig. 6.2(a). The drawing for the part is given in Fig. 6.2(b).

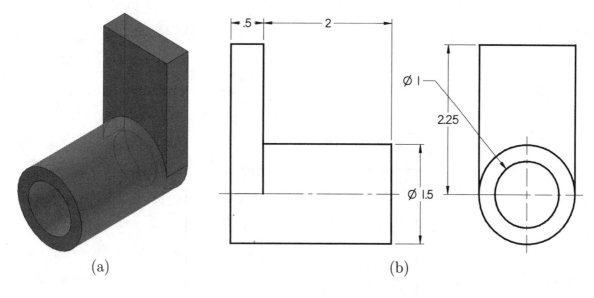

Fig. 6.2

1. Create the part shown in Fig. 6.2(b) using two protrusions.

2. Begin the *Rib* ℞ command.

3. Select your profile plane to be parallel to the frontal view of the drawing in Fig. 6.2(b) and passing through the centre of the cylinder (Fig. 6.3).

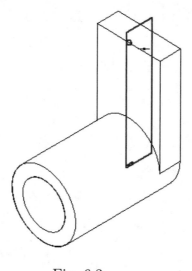

Fig. 6.3

4. Draw the open profile shown in Fig. 6.4.

The next two steps of the rib command, direction and side, will be examined in more detail. In the direction step, you can choose one of four different directions: on the side of the profile in the profile plane or in the direction of the profile plane normal. This step determines in which direction the profile will be swept.

5. Click on *Return* to go to the direction step.

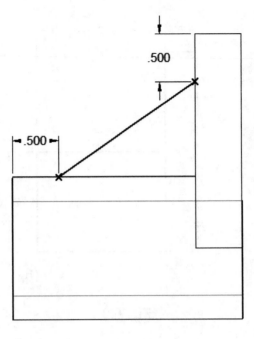

Fig. 6.4

6 | Position the mouse pointer over the part until you see the selection in Fig. 6.5(a) (with the arrow pointing toward the part) and click.

7 | Enter a *Thickness* of 0.25.

8 | In the side step make the selection shown in Fig. 6.5(b) (with two arrows).

9 | Click on *Finish*.

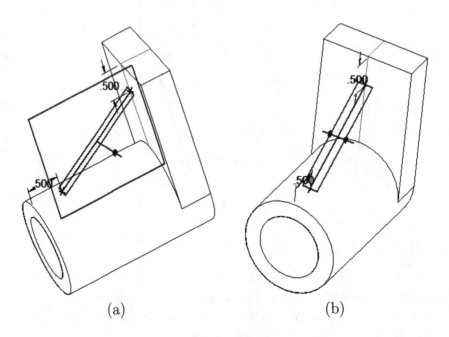

(a)   (b)

Fig. 6.5

The side step determines where the thickness of the rib will be. It is always chosen in a direction normal to the direction chosen in the direction step. If you complete the rib as is, you will get a solid rib by default. You could have done this exactly in the same way with the protrusion step.

Instead, consider an additional option that shows up in the direction (Fig. 6.6(a)) and side step (Fig. 6.6(b)) ribbon bars. By default the *Extend to Next*  icon is selected.

(a)

(b)

Fig. 6.6

10 Select *Rib Finite Depth* 🖻.
11 Enter a *Depth* value of *0.125*.

You will get the part shown in Fig. 6.7. If in the direction step you had chosen your direction opposite and away from the part and had selected the *Extend to Next* 🖻 icon, your part would have failed because there would have been no "next" surface or feature.

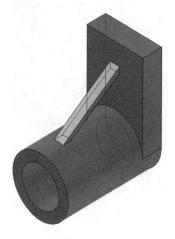

Fig. 6.7

To further examine the effect of the direction step, go back to this step in your part.

12 Click on *Direction Step* ✳.
13 Select the direction shown in Fig. 6.8(a) — normal to the profile plane.
14 Select the side shown in the Fig. 6.8(b).

Your part will resemble Fig. 6.9 if you have selected *Finite Depth* instead of the *Extend to Next* option. The feature will fail if you do not have this option selected because there is no surface or feature to halt the sweep.

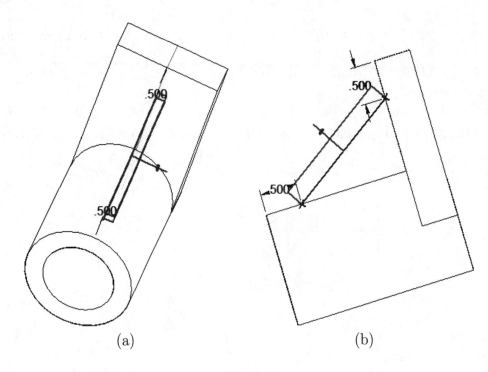

(a)   (b)

Fig. 6.8

Fig. 6.9

6.2   Thread

A threaded hole is achieved with the use of the *Hole* command. You could create a part representing a hex nut with this command. To create a thread on the "outside" of a cylinder such as you would find on a bolt you must use the *Thread* Thread command. You will find this command "underneath," or on the flyout (Fig. 6.10) associated with the *Hole* Hole command.

To learn this command try creating the square head bolt shown in Fig. 6.11. The drawing is given in inches. Create your part in inches; otherwise, you will not be able to reproduce the thread. Use the following steps.

Fig. 6.10

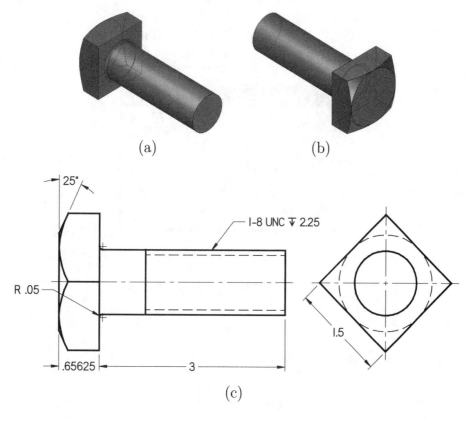

(a) (b)

(c)

Fig. 6.11

1 Create a square *Protrusion* Protru.. for the head of the bolt.

2 Create a cylindrical *Protrusion* Protru.. centred on the square face of the first protrusion.

3 Use a revolved cutout Revol.. at the angle indicated to get the "round" on the head.

4 Add the fillet using *Round* Round.

5 Verify your part (minus the thread) against the physical properties given in Table 6.1 using *Inspect→Physical Properties* from the menu bar.

6 Click on *Thread* Thread.

When you begin the thread feature, you will be presented with the dialogue box shown in Fig. 6.12. Most often you will leave the option untouched. Most thread features are applied to a cylindrical surface. The other option is a *Taper* which is a cone surface.

7 Click on *OK*.

Now you will see the ribbon bar in Fig. 6.13. The steps for this command are:

Table 6.1

Volume		3.8132 inch^3
Surface Area		17.536 inch^2
	K1	1.1709 inch
Radii of Gyration	K2	1.1709 inch
	K3	0.46694 inch

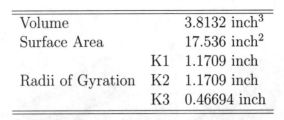

Fig. 6.12

Fig. 6.13

1. *Thread Options* 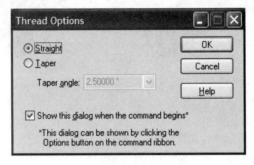,
2. *Select Cylinder Step* ,
3. *Cylinder End Step,* , and
4. *Parameters Step* .

The thread options let you change the thread type by popping up the dialogue box you saw initially (Fig. 6.12). In the select cylinder step you must select a cylindrical surface to which to apply the thread.

8 Select the shaft of the bolt.

In the cylinder end step you must select the end at which your thread will begin. If your thread extends the entire length of the cylinder it does not matter which end you choose.

9 Select the bottom of the cylinder, that is, the end farthest from the head.

Now you must define several parameters. According to the detail drawing (Fig. 6.11(c)), your thread extends 2.25 inches.

10 In the ribbon bar (Fig. 6.14) enter a *Finite value Depth* of 2.25 in.

The *Offset* should be zero since the thread begins at the end of the bolt you selected. Alternatively, you could have selected the other end of the cylinder in the cylinder end step and then entered an appropriate offset and set the depth to *Cylinder extent*.

Fig. 6.14

Notice that on the *Type* of thread pull-down (Fig. 6.15) there is a short list of options. Threads only come in standard sizes or diameters because the tools used to manufacture threads only come in standard sizes. Select the size that matches the callout on the detail drawing Fig. 6.11(c). If you attempt to select a thread diameter that Solid Edge does not have on file, your thread feature will fail. Similarly, if you change the diameter of a cylinder that has an associated thread it will be flagged with a red exclamation mark in the Feature Pathfinder and will no longer be a computed part of your part model.

Fig. 6.15

[11] Check your physical properties.

Although you have added a thread feature the physical properties remain unchanged. If you look at the shaft of the bolt, you will see that the green colour denoting a thread runs all the way to the head of the bolt even though your thread does not extend along the entire length. This is normal.

6.3 Chamfer

A **chamfer** is a bevel applied to an edge; its function is to remove a sharp corner to make a part safer or more attractive. An example is shown at the end of the bolt in Fig. 6.16. In Solid Edge the *Chamfer* Chamfer feature is found on the flyout (Fig. 6.17) for the *Round* Round feature.

Apply a chamfer feature to the bolt you made in Section 6.2 according to the specification in Fig. 6.16(b). Once you start the feature, you will see the ribbon bar shown in Fig. 6.18. There is only one step, *Edge Select* .

By default, the chamfer assumes that both your setbacks are equal. To change this setting, select the *Options* icon on the ribbon bar and then make a selection in the *Chamfer Options* dialogue box, Fig. 6.19. Then return to the chamfer *Edge Select Step* and select the edges you wish to have chamfered. Enter the setback information in the ribbon bar and then click the *Accept* icon. The *Deselect* icon will deselect all edges you have highlighted.

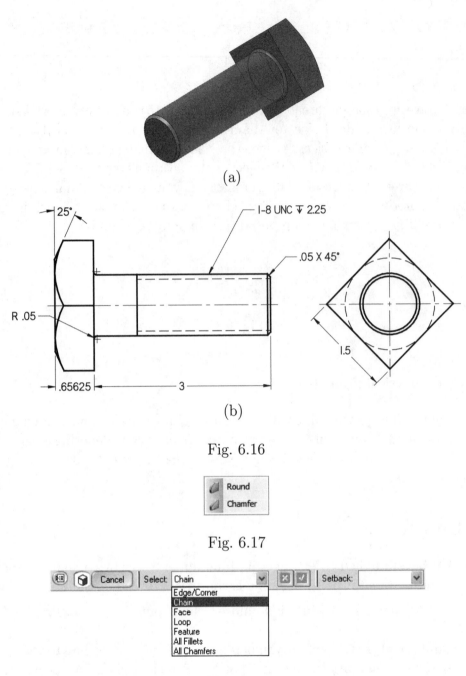

(a)

(b)

Fig. 6.16

Fig. 6.17

Fig. 6.18

6.4 Mirror

With the *Mirror Copy Feature* Mirror.., you can duplicate one or more features belonging to a part by reflecting them in a plane. This feature can save you a lot of time and effort in creating parts or features of parts that have a lot of symmetry. Take, for example, the part shown in Fig. 6.20(a). In the example, the four "ears" of the part should ostensibly only be drawn once and then duplicated. Furthermore, the part clearly demonstrates symmetry about its longitudinal axis.

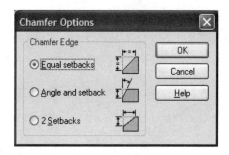

Fig. 6.19

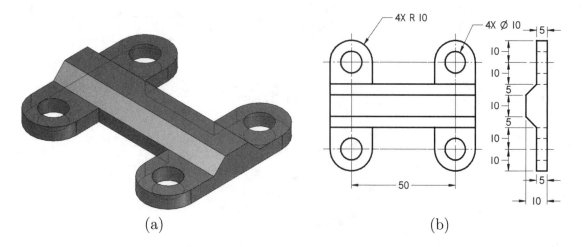

(a)   (b)

Fig. 6.20

Create this part using the drawing in Fig. 6.20(b).

| 1 | Create a new part.
| 2 | Create the protrusion shown in Fig. 6.21(a) based on the profile in Fig. 6.21(b).
| 3 | Create the protrusion shown in Fig. 6.22.
| 4 | Start the *Mirror Copy Feature* Mirror .. command.

You will see the ribbon bar shown in Fig. 6.23. The steps for this feature are:

1. *Select Features Step* , and
2. *Plane Step* .

Begin by selecting the features you wish to include in this mirror feature. You can either select the features in the Feature Pathfinder or in the model area.

| 5 | Select the second protrusion feature.
| 6 | Click on *Accept* .

The *Deselect* icon will deselect all the features you have selected.
     You will be taken to the plane step.

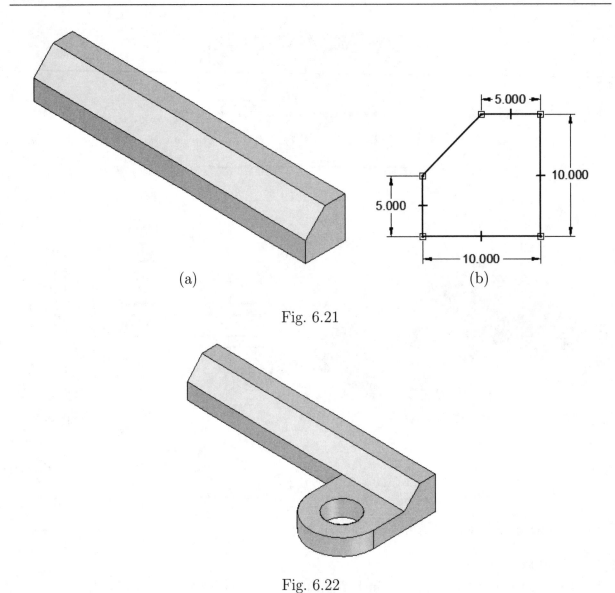

(a)   (b)

Fig. 6.21

Fig. 6.22

| 🔲🔲 Finish | 🔲 🔲 | Name: | MirrorCopy_1 |

Fig. 6.23

⑦ Select a face parallel to the profile view of Fig. 6.20(b) and passing through the midpoint of the length of the part. See Fig. 6.24.

You will get the error message in Fig. 6.25. This is normal. Correct the problem.

⑧ Select *Smart* 🔲 on the ribbon bar.

By default Solid Edge uses the *Fast* 🔲 option. From experience, this rarely works.

⑨ Click on *Preview*.
⑩ Click on *Finish*.

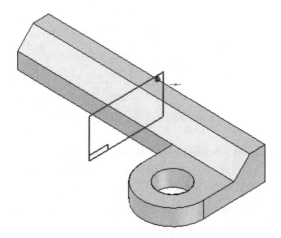

Fig. 6.24

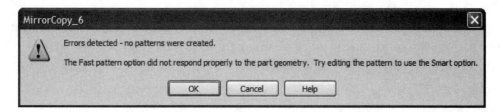

Fig. 6.25

Your part will look like Fig. 6.26. If you happened to choose both features to be part of this mirror feature, then you will see a grey arrow next to the mirror feature in the Feature Pathfinder. The warning will read *Some of the resulting features do not add or remove any material.* The first feature is not mirrored because the mirror plane cuts it in half. Your model is not affected by this error.

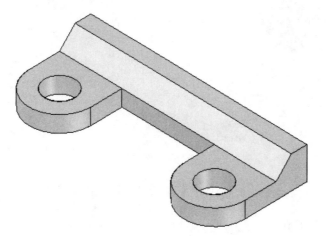

Fig. 6.26

Complete the part with one more mirror feature.

11 Begin another mirror feature.

[12] Select all existing features.

[13] Select the appropriate plane.

[14] Click on *Smart* [⊞↓].

[15] Click on *Preview*.

[16] Click on *Finish*.

The mirror copy feature is **associative**. This means that if any of its constituent features are modified, all the duplicated features will be modified too. If you modified the hole in Fig. 6.22 to be larger, then all the other three holes would immediately change too. The effect is similar if you delete a feature that is part of a mirror copy feature.

6.5   Pattern

Another useful capability for copying features is the Solid Edge *Pattern* ʳₚ Pattern command. One or more features can be duplicated in a rectangular or circular planar pattern. The part shown in Fig. 6.27 is an example of where such a feature is useful.

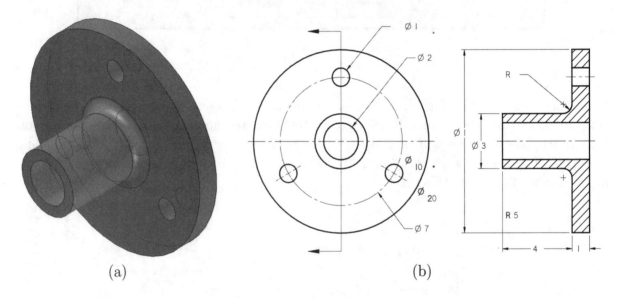

(a)   (b)

Fig. 6.27

[1] Create a new part.

[2] Create a revolved protrusion with the profile in Fig. 6.28(a).

Your part will resemble Fig. 6.28(b).

[3] Create one hole as per the drawing in Fig. 6.27(b) using a hole feature.

Your part will resemble Fig. 6.29.

[4] Click on the *Pattern* ʳₚ Pattern command.

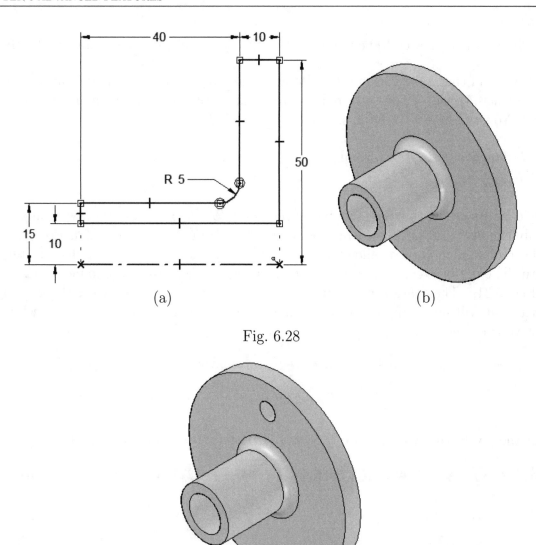

(a)   (b)

Fig. 6.28

Fig. 6.29

Fig. 6.30

The ribbon bar for the pattern command is shown in Fig. 6.30. It resembles the mirror copy feature ribbon bar. The steps are very similar:

1. *Select Step* 📋,
2. *Plane or Sketch Step* 📦, and
3. *Draw Profile Step* 📐.

[5] Choose only the hole feature.

[6] Click on *Accept* ☑.

|7| Choose the diameter 100 circular face as the profile plane in the plane or sketch step.

Solid Edge will then take you into the *Draw Profile Step*, where you must draw a profile to indicate where copies of your selected features will be placed and how many copies will be created. You will have two options:

1. *Rectangular Pattern* Recta.. and
2. *Circular Pattern* Circul...

These icons appear on the draw tool bar in the *Draw Profile Step*. These draw commands are the only effective drawing commands — all others will simply create construction geometry.

The rectangular pattern allows you to lay out the features in a regular or staggered pattern. The options to set the number and spacing of the features are found on the ribbon bar, Fig. 6.31. These are self-explanatory. When you go to draw with the rectangular pattern, you will be prompted to locate and orient a rectangle on the profile which will anchor your pattern.

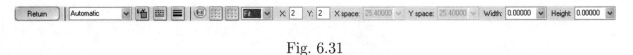

Fig. 6.31

For the given part, you will use the circular pattern command (Fig. 6.32).

Fig. 6.32

|8| Click on *Circular Pattern* Circul...
|9| Click on the centre of the part to anchor the centre of the pattern.
|10| Click again on the centre of the diameter 10 hole to set the radius of the pattern.
|11| Click once more to set a direction.
|12| Enter a *Count* of 3. See Fig. 6.33.
|13| Click on *Return*.
|14| Click on *Finish*.

Notice that although you chose three as your feature count, that includes the existing feature. Similar to the mirror copy feature, the pattern feature is associative. Any change to a constituent feature will be automatically propagated to the duplicated features.

6.6   Sketches

Solid Edge's *Sketch* Sketch ability makes it easy to create multiple features from profiles on the same plane. When you start the command, you must select a plane and then you can

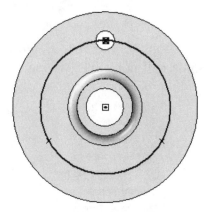

Fig. 6.33

create your sketch. The sketch does not contribute anything to your model because it has no volume. However, it is easy to make a feature based on all or part of the sketch. When you create another feature, you can include elements of the sketch in the profile plane of your new feature. This assumes that the sketch plane and profile plane are not normal to one another. Any element appears as projected into your profile plane in a direction normal to the profile plane. Use the *Include* command on the draw menu to create an associative link between elements in the sketch and your new profile. When you select this command, you will see the dialogue box shown in Fig. 6.34. Unless you want the included geometry to be offset, just click *OK*. Then click on the geometry elements from the sketch and they will be automatically added to your profile. Solid Edge will draw a link handle on each element you include to denote the associative relationship between the element in the profile and the sketch. An entire sketch can be included in a feature that requires a profile simply by selecting the sketch instead of a reference plane during feature creation.

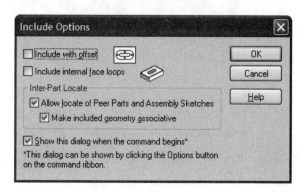

Fig. 6.34

6.7 Reference Planes

Normally, you select reference planes for profiles and for mirroring. However, on occasion creating a reference plane can be useful as an intermediate measure. Solid Edge provides a host of methods for creating reference planes as a stand-alone feature. These commands (Fig. 6.35) are found "underneath" the *Coincident Plane* 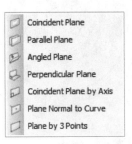 coinci.. icon. Creating a reference plane using any of these commands will not affect your model.

Fig. 6.35

6.8   Construction Display

As your part becomes more complicated and your proficiency improves, you may wish to unclutter the model area by hiding certain elements (Fig. 6.36). The *Construction Display* Constr.. allows you to show or hide commonly used elements such as reference planes, sketches, and your design body. Alternatively, if you right-click in the Feature Pathfinder, you can do the same with the *Show All* and *Hide All* commands.

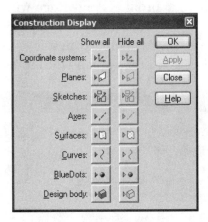

Fig. 6.36

Exercises

1. All exercises for this chapter are located at www.pearsoned.ca/text/fleisig. For each exercise, download it, read it, and create a Solid Edge part to reproduce the part in the drawing exactly. All exercises show one fully dimensioned multiview projection of a part. When creating these parts consider the following.

    (a) When you see a section view of a round part or feature consider using a Revolved Protrusion feature.

    (b) Look for symmetry in the part. Do not repeat the same feature if you can use the Mirror Copy Part or Pattern features.

2. Create Solid Edge parts from measurements of these common products.

    (a) A coffee mug

    (b) A pop can

    (c) A pen

    (d) A CD or DVD

    (e) A CD or DVD jewel case

    (f) A key

    (g) A bowling pin

    (h) A woodscrew

    (i) A washer

    (j) A nut

    (k) A lock washer

PART II

ASSEMBLY MODELLING

CHAPTER 7

Assembly Environment

Learning Objectives

After completing this chapter, you will be able to:

1. Create a new assembly document.
2. Select an assembly template.
3. Open and save assembly documents.
4. Navigate the Assembly Pathfinder.
5. Paint assemblies.
6. Change the viewpoint of an assembly.
7. Modify the display of an assembly.
8. Create and apply 3D view styles to an assembly.
9. Save a rendered image of an assembly.
10. Check the interference of an assembly.
11. Edit parts in place.

An **assembly** is a functional arrangement of parts in space. Assemblies are rigid, that is, the designer does not model how parts move with respect to one another, but only models their spatial position and orientation with respect to one another. For assemblies where the parts are intended to be moving, the designer models the operating position of the parts.

A top-level assembly may be as complicated as an automobile — composed of thousands of parts — or as simple as a screwdriver with no moving parts.

Solid Edge provides the *Assembly Environment* for creating and editing assemblies. To create an assembly, you will open a new assembly document, add existing parts to it, and specify assembly relationships between parts. Modelling the motion of moving parts is accomplished in *Applications→Motion*, which is beyond the scope of this manual. Much of this chapter mirrors the introduction to the part environment in Chapter 2.

7.1   Templates

To enter the assembly environment, you must create a new assembly document. Create a new assembly document in the same manner as a part document, except that you must choose an assembly template. All assembly templates and documents have a *.asm* extension. The available assembly template files are listed in Table 7.1. Note that *Normal.asm* is a copy of either *Normeng.asm* or *Normmet.asm* depending on the installation options selected. The dimensions of parts will remain in their original units when you add them to your assembly. The selection of template only has an effect on the default units and dimension style for the assembly itself.

Table 7.1

Template Name	Default Units	Default Dimension Style
Normal.asm	Installation Dependent	
Normeng.asm	inches	ANSI
Normmet.asm	millimetres	ISO

7.2   User Interface

After creating a new assembly document, take a few minutes to familiarize yourself with the user interface of the assembly environment as illustrated in Fig. 7.1. Note the *Assembly* label in the titlebar of the window. The menu bar, ribbon bar, status bar, main tool bar, and model area are effectively unchanged from those in the part environment. The features toolbar has been replaced with an *Assembly Commands* toolbar. The EdgeBar now contains some new tabs, two of which you will use regularly. The *Assembly Pathfinder* tab ⬚ is similar to the Features Pathfinder in that it maintains an up-to-date list of the parts contained in your assembly document. The *Parts Library* tab ⬚ allows you to navigate through the files on your computer to find and select parts for addition to the assembly.

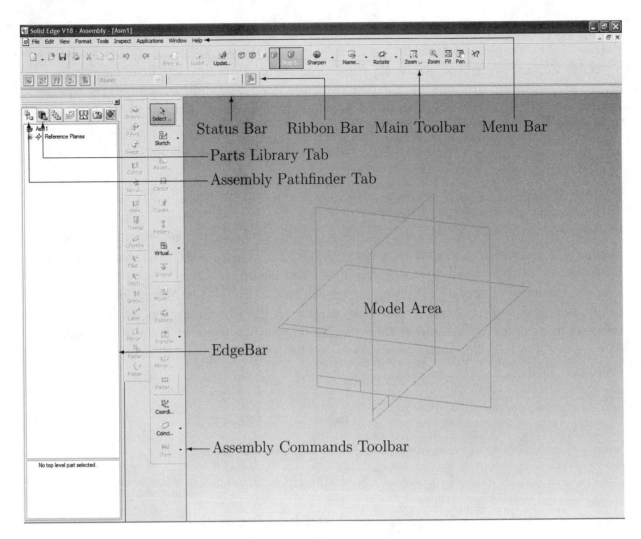

Fig. 7.1

7.3 Assembly Documents

1 Open the assembly file *Coffee Pot.asm* in *C:\Program Files\Solid Edge V18\Training* (or equivalent directory on your computer).

Your screen should appear similar to Fig. 7.2. By opening this assembly file you have also automatically opened its constituent part and subassembly files.

2 Click on the *Assembly Pathfinder* tab in the EdgeBar.

You will see this assembly is composed of three parts, *Coffee Pot.par*, *Strap Handle.par*, and *handle.par*, and one subassembly, *strainer.asm*. This means that when you would like to copy an assembly, you must include its top-level assembly files plus its constituent part files and subassemblies. For each subassembly (and there is no limit to the number of levels of subassemblies), you must copy their constituent part files too.

It is recommended that when you create assemblies you place them in the same directory. Furthermore, once assemblies and parts are created, do not rename the files. If you have

Fig. 7.2

included a part in your assembly and then you rename it, Solid Edge will not be able to find the part file. Similarly, once assemblies are created, do not move the part files relative to the assembly files to which they are associated. Again, if you do, Solid Edge will not be able to find them.

When you save the assembly file, the file appears with the icon shown in Fig. 7.3(a) in Windows Explorer. In addition, Solid Edge saves a configuration file with a *.cfg* extension like the one shown in Fig. 7.3(b). Your configuration file icon may be different from the one shown. The configuration file contains **display configuration** information associated with the assembly file of the same name. Display configurations will be explained later with respect to engineering drawings. Unless you are creating drawings, you may delete the configuration files and Solid Edge will automatically recreate them.

7.4   Creating, Adding, and Editing Parts

With *Coffee Pot.asm* open, try adding a part to the assembly.

3 Click on the *Parts Library* tab ▧ in the EdgeBar.

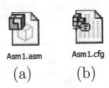

Asm1.asm   Asm1.cfg
  (a)   (b)

Fig. 7.3

In the EdgeBar you will see a directory listing. Clicking on directories takes you down a level and clicking on *Up One Level* ⬆ takes you up a directory level.

4 Navigate to *C:\Program Files\Solid Edge V18\Training* (or equivalent directory on your computer).

5 Select part file *bolt1.par*.

6 Drag this file and drop it in the model area. Anywhere in the model area is fine.

You will notice the part will appear faintly in the model area, as shown in Fig. 7.4(a), depending on where in the model area you dropped the part. Verify that the part has actually been added to the assembly.

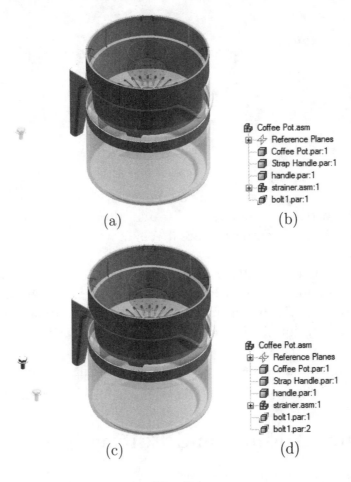

Fig. 7.4

7 Click on the *Assembly Pathfinder* tab ⬚.

Your list of parts should be identical to Fig. 7.4(b).

8 Click on the *Parts Library* tab ⬚.

9 Drag and drop another *bolt1.par* into the model area.

10 Click on the *Assembly Pathfinder* tab ⬚.

Your assembly will appear as shown in Fig. 7.4(c) and Assembly Pathfinder as shown in Fig. 7.4(d). You will notice that in the Assembly Pathfinder *bolt1.par* appears twice: once followed by *:1* and the second time by *:2*. These numbers indicate an **instance** number. Solid Edge does not require you to create a separate part for each instance of a given part. You just add the same part more than once to the assembly and Solid Edge increments this number to tell you how many instances of the particular part are in the assembly. Incidentally, the same part can be used in multiple assemblies.

To edit parts that are part of any assembly you do not have to open the part file by using the *Open* ⬚ command. Just select the part you wish to edit either in the model area using the *Select Tool* select.. or by clicking on it in the Assembly Pathfinder. Right-click in the menu and select either *Edit* or *Open in Solid Edge Part*. The *Edit* function will open the part environment for the selected part but the assembly will not be hidden. If you use the *Open in Solid Edge Part* function the assembly will be hidden. If you modify either instance of *bolt1.par* from above in this manner the other instance of the same part will be automatically updated when you exit the part environment by clicking *File→Close and Return* or *File→Close* from the menu bar.

Normally, your workflow for assemblies will be to create the parts first and then to create the assembly. Sometimes you will wish to create a part when you have a portion of the assembly created. In the *Parts Library* tab of the EdgeBar, Solid Edge has the command *Create In-Place* ⬚ for creating parts directly in an assembly.

7.5 Assembly Pathfinder Navigation

Solid Edge provides a number of practical commands on the context menu of the Assembly Pathfinder. To get the context menu of Fig. 7.5 right-click on an item (reference plane, part, or subassembly) in the Assembly Pathfinder.

The first two commands, *Delete* and *Rename*, are self-explanatory. *Expand* and *Collapse* are equivalent to clicking the plus and minus signs next to the assembly files in the Assembly Pathfinder. The plus expands the list of constituent parts for an assembly and the minus hides them.

The commands *Show* to *Show Only* allow you selectively to show and hide parts of your assembly. Even simple assemblies can be difficult to work with. Use these commands to unclutter your display and make working with the assembly easier.

Use *Activate* when parts are greyed-out in the Assembly Pathfinder. Sometimes, Solid Edge will load parts inactivated when you open an assembly. Inactive parts occupy less memory and are not editable. Some functions like interference checking (see Section 7.7) require parts to be activated.

Fig. 7.5

Some commands in this context menu will act on multiple items in the Assembly Pathfinder if you select the items while holding down the *Ctrl* key and then right-click.

7.6 Viewing

The commands you are familiar with from the part environment for changing viewpoint, rendering an image, editing and applying 3D view styles, painting, etc., are identical in the assembly environment and thus will receive no further treatment in this chapter.

The assembly environment is host to one new capability not available in the part environment: *Applications→Virtual Studio* on the menu bar. Virtual Studio will produce an animated video of your assembly in which the viewpoint position and direction move.

7.7   Interference Checking

An **interference** in an assembly occurs when two or more parts overlap. In the real world this cannot happen — two parts cannot occupy the same volume. But in the virtual world of Solid Edge, interference is not automatically checked. Consequently, you will wish to do so manually.

$\boxed{11}$ Click on *Inspect→Check Interference* on the menu bar.

You will get the ribbon bar shown in Fig. 7.6. The basic steps are:

Fig. 7.6

1. select options,
2. select the parts and subassemblies, and
3. execute the interference check.

$\boxed{12}$ Click *Interference Options* ⊞ in the ribbon bar.

You will get a dialogue box.

$\boxed{13}$ Set the options suggested in Fig. 7.7(a) on the *Options* tab.
$\boxed{14}$ Set the options suggested in Fig. 7.7(b) on the *Report* tab.
$\boxed{15}$ Click on *OK*.
$\boxed{16}$ Select all the parts and the subassembly in the Assembly Pathfinder.

Unfortunately, there is no way to quickly select multiple parts.

$\boxed{17}$ Click on *Process*.

With these options and selections, Solid Edge will check the interference between all pairs of parts and parts in subassemblies. If there is no interference found, Solid Edge will answer with the dialogue box Fig. 7.8. Otherwise, it will create an interference part. This interference part is added to your assembly and contains the volumes resulting from the Boolean intersection of all pairs of parts. When you are done with an interference part, delete it from your assembly and delete the file from your computer.

Interfering parts will be highlighted in the Assembly Pathfinder and parts with no interference are dimmed in the model. Solid Edge also produces a *report.txt* file (Fig. 7.9).

With the recommended options for interference checking, Solid Edge will not detect interferences due to threaded features. If this option is unchecked, Solid Edge will report an interference between each pair of threaded parts such as a nut on a bolt.

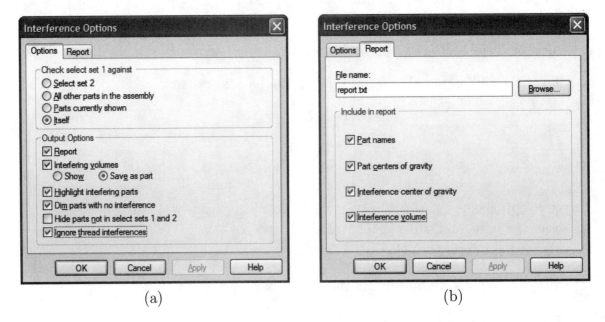

(a)   (b)

Fig. 7.7

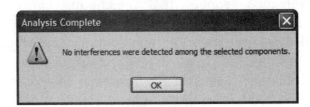

Fig. 7.8

```
Report Name: report.txt Report Time: 13/6/2006 16:31:42 Report
Options:
    Part Names
    Part CG's
    Interference CG's
    Interference Volumes

Select Set #1:
    strainer.asm:1
    handle.par:1
    Strap Handle.par:1
    Coffee Pot.par:1

Interferences:
1 of 2
    Strainer Body.par:1
    Located at:         0.000 in        0.000 in        4.043 in
    Strainer Top.par:1
    Located at:         0.000 in        0.000 in        5.018 in
    Interference Volume 0.000 in^3
    Located at:        -2.095 in        0.000 in        5.277 in
    Interference Volume 0.000 in^3
    Located at:        -2.078 in        0.000 in        5.324 in
    Interference Volume 0.000 in^3
    Located at:         0.000 in       -2.095 in        5.277 in
    Interference Volume 0.000 in^3
    Located at:         0.000 in       -2.078 in        5.324 in
    Interference Volume 0.000 in^3
    Located at:         2.095 in        0.000 in        5.277 in
    Interference Volume 0.000 in^3
    Located at:         2.078 in        0.000 in        5.324 in
    Interference Volume 0.000 in^3
    Located at:         0.000 in        2.095 in        5.277 in
    Interference Volume 0.000 in^3
    Located at:         0.000 in        2.078 in        5.324 in

2 of 2
    handle.par:1
    Located at:        -3.120 in        0.001 in        2.065 in
    Strap Handle.par:1
    Located at:        -0.113 in        0.000 in        2.854 in
    Interference Volume 0.000 in^3
    Located at:        -2.535 in       -0.125 in        2.854 in

2 Interferences Detected
```

Fig. 7.9

CHAPTER 8

Assembly Relationships

Learning Objectives

After completing this chapter, you will be able to:

1. Count the degrees of freedom of an assembly.
2. Create the Mate, Planar Align, Axial Align, Insert, and Ground assembly relationships.
3. Modify assembly relationships.
4. Fully constrain an assembly.

In the last chapter you learned the basics of the Assembly Environment. You should be reasonably comfortable with the Assembly Environment. In this chapter, you will learn how to create fully constrained assemblies, given a set of parts. The exercises at the end of the chapter will ask you to test that knowledge by assembling and creating parts from a set of working drawings. The assembly will be drawn in isometric view, both exploded and assembled.

Creating fully constrained assemblies will be explained with the aid of the example assembly in Fig. 8.1(a).

1. Create Top Block as per the drawing Fig. 8.1(b). Save it with the filename *Top Block.par*.

2. Create Bottom Block as per the drawing Fig. 8.1(c). Save it with the filename *Bottom Block.par*.

3. Create Screw as per the drawing Fig. 8.1(d). The hexagon is "regular" (i.e., all sides and angles are equal) and is centred. Save it with the filename *Screw.par*.

All dimensions are in millimetres. The goal of this chapter is help you to build this assembly fully constrained and without interference.

8.1 Degrees of Freedom

To explain how an assembly is to be fully constrained you must understand Degrees of Freedom (DOFs) in the context of the assembly environment. With profiles, as you may remember, each two-dimensional element has a number of DOFs, depending on the element

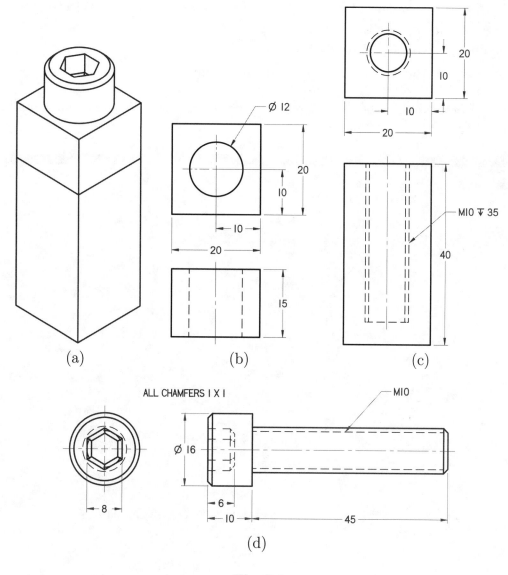

Fig. 8.1

type (i.e., three for circles, four for lines, etc.). The goal of a fully constrained assembly is to fix all DOFs such that the part's position and orientation in space are fully constrained. From basic mechanics, a rigid body such as a part has six DOFs: three DOFs for translation or position motion and three DOFs for orientation or rotational motion. Solid Edge provides a set of assembly relationships with which to constrain these DOFs.

8.2 Ground Assembly Relationship

4 Create a new assembly using the *Normmet.asm* template.

5 Add Bottom Block to the assembly.

6 | Hide the reference planes by right-clicking in the model area and selecting *Hide All→ Reference Planes* from the context menu.

7 | Click on the *Assembly Pathfinder* tab.

8 | Select Bottom Block by clicking on it in the model area.

The edges of Bottom Block should become highlighted in yellow. Your screen should appear as shown in Fig. 8.2.

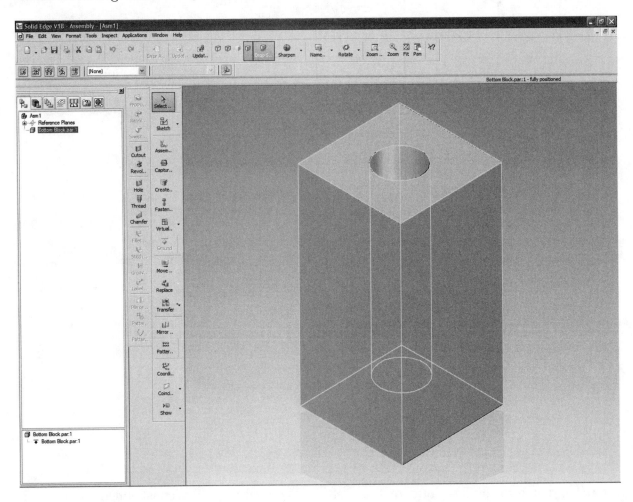

Fig. 8.2

Notice the phrase *fully positioned* in the status bar. Similarly, the ▱ icon in the Assembly Pathfinder indicates that all DOFs of your first part are fixed. This is the case because for the first part of your assembly Solid Edge automatically adds a *Ground* assembly relationship to the part. Look in the ♦ icon in the bottom left-hand corner of Fig. 8.2. This icon indicates that the *Ground* assembly relationship has been added to your part.

The ground relationship could also have been added manually with the *Ground* Ground command. Its icon is found on the assembly commands toolbar. You can have an arbitrary number of parts with this relationship in an assembly. You must have at least one ground relationship in your assembly to fully constrain the assembly.

8.3 Move Part Command

9   Click on the *Parts Library* tab.

10 Add Top Block to the assembly.

11 Click on the *Assembly Pathfinder* tab.

12 Click on *Select Tool* Select...

13 Select Top Block by clicking on it in the model area.

Your screen will look like Fig. 8.3, although your parts will be located differently and displayed at a different zoom. Notice the phrase *not positioned* in the status bar and the icon in the Assembly Pathfinder. These both indicate that the current part is not fully positioned but do not tell you how many unfixed DOFs remain. Look at the bottom of the Assembly Pathfinder pane. Because there are no assembly relationships listed here for Top Block, you must have six DOFs to fix.

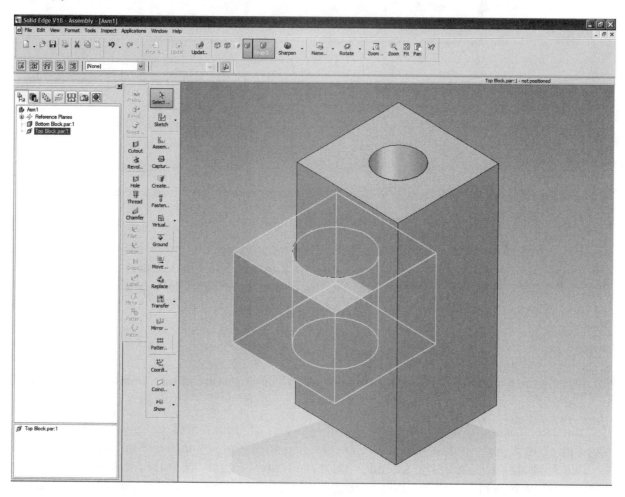

Fig. 8.3

To help ascertain which DOFs are unfixed for any given part try "moving" Top Block.

14 Click on *Move Part* Move...

15 When you see Fig. 8.4 click *OK*.

16 Make sure that the *Free Form Move*  button is depressed on the ribbon bar (Fig. 8.5).

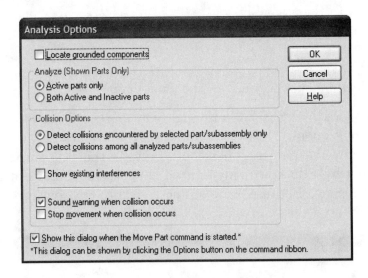

Fig. 8.4

Fig. 8.5

Because Top Block was selected prior to starting the command you do not have to select it.

17 Click and drag your mouse pointer in the model area.

Top Block will move with your mouse pointer. As you add assembly relationships this motion will be restricted — the assembly relationships will be respected by the move part command. The move part command is a very useful way to determine which DOFs of a part or assembly are unconstrained.

18 Click on *Select Part* on the ribbon bar.

19 Select Bottom Block.

20 Try to move Bottom Block by clicking and dragging your mouse pointer in the model area.

Bottom Block is *fully positioned* and grounded and therefore will not move. You cannot move grounded parts unless you select *Locate grounded components* in Fig. 8.4.

The next step is to add the assembly relationships necessary to fully constrain Top Block in the assembly. This will be done using *Mate*, *Axial Align*, and *Planar Align* assembly relationships. Before you begin adding the assembly relationships look at the assembly drawing Fig. 8.1(a). Notice the two block parts are flush (not interfering), one on top of the other. For the assembly to work, the holes in both parts must be aligned and both parts are turned or oriented about the holes in the same way. You will reproduce this positioning using the above relationships.

8.4   Mate Assembly Relationship

Add a Mate assembly relationship between the two parts.

21 Click on *Select Tool* Select...

22 Select Top Block in the Model Area or Assembly Pathfinder.

23 Click on *Edit Definition* ⟳ in the ribbon bar (Fig. 8.6).

Fig. 8.6

24 In the assembly relationships ribbon bar (Fig. 8.7) click on the black triangle on the right side of the *Relationship Types* ⟳▾ icon.

Fig. 8.7

This will display the drop-down menu in Fig. 8.8.

Fig. 8.8

25 Select *Mate* ▷◁ from the drop-down menu.

The mate assembly relationship requires you to select two planar faces, each on a different part.

26 Select the bottom face of Top Block.

27 Select the top face of Bottom Block.

Use QuickPick to help select the correct faces. Your assembly should resemble Fig. 8.9. An assembly relationship places a constraint on the relative position and orientation of the two parts. A Mate assembly relationship ensures that the two planar faces selected are

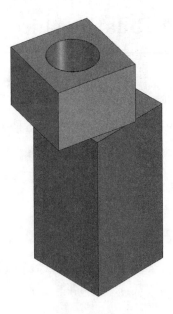

Fig. 8.9

always coplanar such that the two solids are on opposite sides of the common plane. It is like making sure that one part is always touching another where they are flat. To further illustrate this try the Move Part command again. This time change the orientation of the assembly so that you are viewing it from a direction where the two faces involved in the mate are normal to your screen. Use the *Named Views* Name.. command to select the appropriate view. Your model should resemble Fig. 8.10.

Fig. 8.10

Use the Move Part command to move Top Block. You will see that it is restricted to planar motion. The mate relationship has fixed three DOFs. The three remaining DOFs are motion in two directions in the plane and rotation of the part in the plane. Additional relationships are needed to fix the three unfixed DOFs.

8.5   Axial Align Assembly Relationship

Next you will apply the Axial Align assembly relationship to line up the holes of the two parts.

28 Click on *Select Tool* select...

29 Select Top Block in the Model Area or Assembly Pathfinder.

30 Click on *Edit Definition* 🔧.

31 Click on the black triangle on the right side of *Relationship Types* 🔲.

32 Select *Axial Align* 🔗 from the drop-down menu.

33 Select the cylindrical face of Top Block.

34 Select the cylindrical face of Bottom Block.

Your assembly will resemble Fig. 8.11.

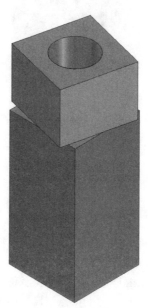

Fig. 8.11

Try the Move Part command again. You will see that the only DOF remaining unfixed is the rotation of the top block about the hole axis. Axial Align removed two DOFs: translation in the plane created by the Mate.

8.6   Planar Align Assembly Relationship

The last unfixed DOF can be eliminated using any number of methods. Try using the Planar Align assembly relationship.

35 | Click on *Select Tool* Select...

36 | Select Top Block in the Model Area or Assembly Pathfinder.

37 | Click on *Edit Definition* ⬚.

38 | Click on the black triangle on the right side of *Relationship Types* ⬚.

39 | Select *Planar Align* ⬚ from the drop-down menu.

40 | Select a vertical planar face of Top Block.

41 | Select a vertical planar face of Bottom Block.

This last relationship should fully constrain the two parts together. Check the icons next to the part names in the Assembly Pathfinder to make sure that both parts are fully constrained. Your assembly should resemble Fig. 8.12.

Fig. 8.12

The Planar Align assembly relationship is very similar to the Mate assembly relationship. In both cases you select two planar faces on different parts and Solid Edge ensures that these two faces remain coplanar. In the case of the Mate assembly relationship the solid side of the two parts is opposite the common plane, and in the case of the Planar Align assembly relationship the solid side is on the same side of the common plane.

8.7 Insert Assembly Relationship

The last remaining step is to add Screw to the assembly and fully constrain it. For fasteners such as screws, bolts, nuts, washers, etc., Solid Edge provides a special assembly relationship, *Insert* ⬚. The Insert assembly relationship requires two pairs of inputs: a pair of cylindrical faces and a pair of planar faces from the same pair of parts.

42 | Add Screw to the assembly.

43   Click on *Select Tool* Select...

44   Select Screw in the Model Area.

45   Click on *Edit Definition* 📇.

46   Click on the black triangle on the right side of *Relationship Types* 🔲▾.

47   Select *Insert* ⚓ from the drop-down menu.

48   Select the cylindrical face of Screw.

49   Select the cylindrical face of Top Block.

50   Select the bottom face of the head of Screw.

51   Select the top face of Top Block.

Your assembly will resemble Fig. 8.13.

Fig. 8.13

52   Select Screw.

Look at the bottom of the Assembly Pathfinder. You will find the list of assembly relationships that Screw is in (Fig. 8.14). You added one relationship, Insert, but two appear. From Table 8.1, these are identified as Mate and Axial Align assembly relationships. The Insert is shorthand for a Mate and Axial Align assembly relationship, hence the need to pick the pairs of cylindrical and planar faces. The Insert relationship differs in two ways from adding the Mate and Axial Align relationships manually. First, the faces you pick must be on the same two parts. You could have chosen your cylindrical faces from Screw and Bottom Block instead of Top Block if you did not use the insert. The second difference is with regard to rotation of the parts about the axis defining the Axial Align. Between the Top Block and

Bottom Block you had to specify a Planar Align to fix this rotation. Insert automatically fixes this rotation angle to whatever it is at the time the insert was created. Note the label *rotation locked* next to the axial align in Fig. 8.14.

AssemblyExample1Screw.par:1
　▸|◂ AssemblyExample1TopBlock.par:1　(0.00 mm)　(V351)
　▸|◦ AssemblyExample1TopBlock.par:1　(rotation locked)

Fig. 8.14

Table 8.1

Relationship	Command Icon	Indicator Icon	Max. DOFs Fixed
Mate	▸|◂	▸|◂	3
Planar Align	▸|▫	▸|▪	3
Axial Align	▸|◉	▸|◦	4
Insert	♻	▸|◂ and ▸|◦	6
Ground	◆ Ground	⟊	6

8.8   Editing Assembly Relationships

A few functions on existing assembly relationships can be executed in the Assembly Pathfinder. Clicking on a part in the Assembly Pathfinder will produce a list of assembly relationships like that in Fig. 8.15. Above the dotted horizontal line, relationships with parent parts are listed. Below the line, relationships with child parts are shown. It is possible for one part to have relationships with more than two parts.

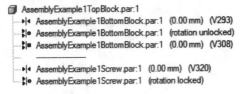

AssemblyExample1TopBlock.par:1
　▸|◂ AssemblyExample1BottomBlock.par:1　(0.00 mm)　(V293)
　▸|◦ AssemblyExample1BottomBlock.par:1　(rotation unlocked)
　▸|▪ AssemblyExample1BottomBlock.par:1　(0.00 mm)　(V308)

　▸|◂ AssemblyExample1Screw.par:1　(0.00 mm)　(V320)
　▸|◦ AssemblyExample1Screw.par:1　(rotation locked)

Fig. 8.15

Right-clicking on a relationship in the bottom of the Assembly Pathfinder will yield a context menu like the one in Fig. 8.16. The *Delete* and *Suppress* commands are intuitive. The *Flip* command is explained in Chapter 9.

To add or modify assembly relationships, use the *Assemble* Assem.. command. Alternatively, use *Select Tool* Select.. to select a part and then click *Edit Definition* 🔧 in the ribbon bar. In the ribbon bar you will find a *Relationship List* — the drop-down menu on the left containing the words *Creating Relationship 1* in Fig. 8.6. At this point, you can add another relationship

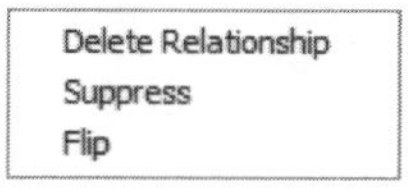

Delete Relationship
Suppress
Flip

Fig. 8.16

by clicking on the *Relationship Types* icon. To edit a relationship simply select it from the *Relationship List* and, as with part environment features, use the QuickStep icons to modify the relationship parameters and selections.

8.9   Assembly Constraintedness

It may have occurred to you that you could construct an assembly by using the *Move Part* Move.. command to place all the parts in your assembly. However, it is unlikely that you will be able to place the parts exactly, especially in more complex assemblies. This leads to three problems. First, your assembly will have poor fit and interference. To someone else the assembly may be unclear, since they may not be sure if you intended for these poor fits and interferences. Second, in more complex assemblies, the manual calculations to determine the position and orientation of parts will be laborious. Third, by not capturing designer intent with assembly relationships, the assembly will be ambiguous.

With profiles you learned to compute and add DOFs. This procedure does not work with assembly relationships. Consider the first two parts added in Fig. 8.13. You added three relationships: Mate, Axial Align, and Planar Align. These in turn fixed three, two, and one DOF for a total of six. This might lead you to believe that these relationships always fix these same numbers of DOFs. However, if you add the Axial Align relationship first you will find that Top Block has only two DOFs remaining: rotation and translation along the axis of rotation. Adding each of the other two relationships would remove only one DOF each. The conclusion that must be drawn is that assembly relationships cannot be added because multiple relationships on a single part often fix the same DOFs. Again from the earlier example, adding the Mate relationship first instead would fix the orientation of the part in all but one direction (rotation about the hole). Adding the Axial Align relationship first also fixed the orientation of the part in all but one direction. No matter the order these two relationships were added, they both would act to fix these two DOFs of orientation. Implicit is that the mating surface is normal to the axis of the Axial Align.

Editing parts may result in broken assembly relationships. A damaged or broken assembly relationship will cause parts to become underconstrained as indicated by ⬗, and the damaged relationship will appear in red in the lower part of the Assembly Pathfinder. Either delete the offending relationship and recreate it or modify it using edit definition. Use the *Error Assistant* Error A.. to help locate and correct problems with your assembly.

Exercises

1. All exercises for this chapter are located at `www.pearsoned.ca/text/fleisig`. For each exercise, download it, read it, and create a Solid Edge assembly and parts to reproduce the product in the drawings exactly. All exercises are composed of an assembly drawing, some completed parts, and detail drawings. Each assembly drawing shows an isometric pictorial of the assembly exploded and/or assembled. The assembly should be fully constrained and free of interference except between threads. When creating these assemblies consider the following:

    (a) Errors in interference are a consequence of errors either in the assembly relationships, the parts themselves, or both.

    (b) Always fully constrain your assembly.

    (c) Always check the inferences in your assembly.

CHAPTER 9

More Assembly Relationships

Learning Objectives

After completing this chapter, you will be able to:

1. Apply and modify the Connect, Parallel, Tangent, and Angle assembly relationships.
2. Use and edit assembly relationship dimensions, the Flip command, Fixed Offsets, Floating Offsets, and Rotation Locking.
3. Create and edit subassemblies.

In the last chapter you learned the most frequently used assembly relationships. In this chapter, you will learn a few of the less commonly used assembly relationships and other features. The exercises at the end of the chapter will ask you to test that knowledge by assembling and creating parts from a set of working drawings. The assembly will be drawn in a multiview both exploded and assembled.

The explanations in this chapter centre around creating assemblies using the parts shown in Fig. 9.1.

1. Create Base as per the drawing in Fig. 9.1(a). Save it with the filename *Base.par*.
2. Create Shaft as per the drawing in Fig. 9.1(b). Save it with the filename *Shaft.par*.
3. Create Handle as per the drawing in Fig. 9.1(c). Note that the thick circle in the profile view is actually two concentric circles very close together. Save it with the filename *Handle.par*.

All dimensions are in millimetres.

9.1 Rotation Locking

Your objective is to create the assembly in Fig. 9.2 using the parts in Fig. 9.1 fitted exactly as shown. The assembly should be created using assembly relationships and, as before, the completed assembly must be fully constrained and there must be no interferences, except between threaded features.

1. Create a new assembly from the template *Normeng.asm*.

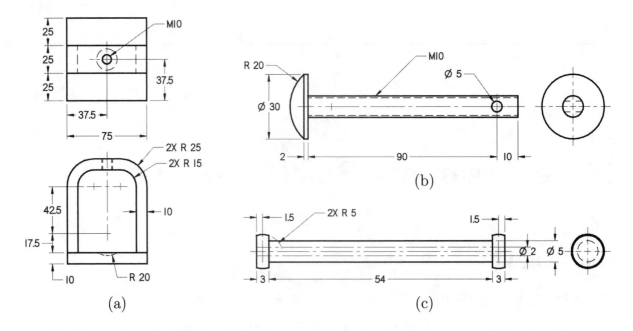

Fig. 9.1

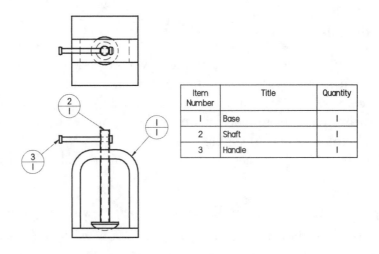

Fig. 9.2

The units are by default in English (inches) and dimensions are displayed using the ANSI style. Since the parts are in millimetres, change the length units to millimetres.

2 Select *File→File Properties→Units* from the menu bar.

3 Change the *Length Readout Unit* to *mm*.

4 Change the *Area Readout* to *mm ˆ2*.

5 Click on *Advanced Units*.

6 Change *Volume* to *mm ˆ3*.

This will ensure that assembly dimensions appear in the correct units and dimension style and that the results of interference checks are also in the same units as the parts.

7 Add Base to the assembly.

8 Add Shaft and Handle to the assembly.

Add Base first so that it is grounded. Your assembly should resemble Fig. 9.3.

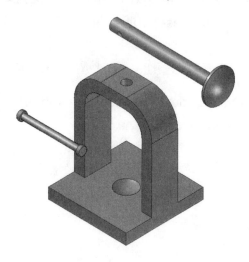

Fig. 9.3

Fix Handle into Shaft.

9 Click on *Assemble* Assem...

10 Select *Axial Align* ⊯.

11 Choose the cylindrical faces of Handle and the hole in Shaft.

Your assembly should resemble Fig. 9.4.

Fig. 9.4

Adding the Axial Align assembly relationship fixes four DOFs in your assembly. Suppose that Shaft is grounded. In that case, Handle has two unfixed DOFs: translation through the hole in Shaft and rotation in that hole. To test, ground Shaft.

12 Select Shaft with *Select Tool* Select...

13 Add a Ground assembly relationship with *Ground* Ground.

14 Use *Move Part* Move.. to test the unfixed DOFs of Handle.

15 When done, delete the Ground assembly relationship on Shaft.

16 Select Handle.

17 In the Assembly Pathfinder, select the Axial Align relationship ⦂•.

Observe the label *rotation unlocked* next to it. In the ribbon bar (Fig. 9.5), notice that the *Rotation Unlocked* ↻ icon is depressed.

Fig. 9.5

18 Click on *Rotation Locked*.

19 Click on *OK*.

You have frozen the angle of Handle in Shaft. That angle is arbitrary since Handle is perfectly symmetrical about its axis. Recall that the Insert assembly relationship automatically locks the rotation of the part inserted. Rotation locking has fixed one DOF of your assembly. Your assembly should resemble Fig. 9.6.

Fig. 9.6

9.2   Tangent Assembly Relationship

The next step is to eliminate the final unfixed DOF of Handle with respect to Shaft. Ideally one would create a Mate assembly relationship between the knob at the end of Handle and the threaded surface of Shaft. However, you can only select planar faces in the Mate assembly relationship and the threaded surface of Shaft is cylindrical. Instead, use the Tangent assembly relationship when one or both of the faces are curved.

20 Click on *Assemble* Assem...

21 Select *Tangent* ▶▷.

22 Select the threaded surface of Shaft.

23 Select one of the annular (two concentric circles that look like a donut) faces of Handle.

Your assembly will resemble Fig. 9.7.

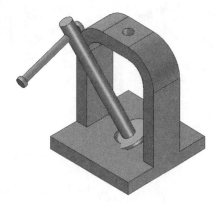

Fig. 9.7

If you count the DOFs fixed in the assembly besides the ground assembly relationship on Base, you should get six. The relationships and rotation lock added so far fully constrain Handle with respect to Shaft. However, Solid Edge still marks both parts as *not positioned* ⬚ because the two parts can move together. Only when a part is fully constrained with respect to a grounded part will Solid Edge consider it to be *fully positioned* ⬚.

9.3 Flip Side

24 Add an Axial Align assembly relationship to line up the hole on Base with the thread of Shaft.

Depending on the relative orientation of Shaft and Base you may find Shaft is upside down, as shown in Fig. 9.8(a). Solid Edge provides an easy solution to this problem. Edit the Axial Align assembly relationship between Base and Shaft. Click the *Flip* button in the ribbon bar. Shaft may disappear. If so, it is off screen. Use the *Fit* ⊠ icon to bring it into view and then use the Move Part command to slide Shaft near Base. This Flip Side command is also available in the Planar Align, Mate, Parallel, and Tangent assembly relationships where it functions similarly. Your assembly should now resemble Fig. 9.8(b).

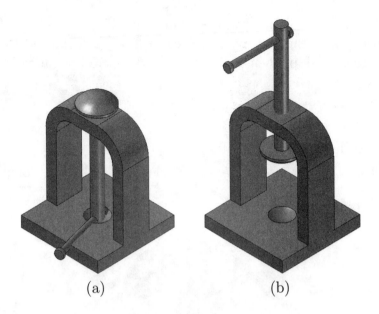

(a)   (b)

Fig. 9.8

9.4   Connect Assembly Relationship

The next step is to sit the bottom of Shaft onto the bottom of Base. The two spherical faces will touch. This is a good place to use a Tangent assembly relationship. It can also be done using the Connect ◾ assembly relationship. The Connect assembly relationship fixes a point on one part to a point on another part. It effectively fixes three DOFs. If one of the parts is grounded then the other part has its three translation DOFs fixed and therefore is able to only rotate about the point specified in the Connect assembly relationship.

Apply the Connect assembly relationship.

25	Click on *Assemble* Assem...
26	Select *Connect* ◾.
27	Select the spherical face of the Shaft.
28	Select the spherical face of the Base.

Solid Edge connects the centres of the two spherical faces. The Connect assembly relationship only works without interference in this case because the two spherical faces have the same radius. Your assembly should resemble Fig. 9.9.

9.5   Angle Assembly Relationship

The assembly now has one unfixed DOF: the angle of Handle with respect to Base. Fixing this angle will also fix the angle of Shaft because earlier Handle and Shaft were fully constrained with respect to one another. Handle should be lined up as shown in Fig. 9.2. Use the Angle ∡ assembly relationship to fix the last unfixed DOF. To apply the Angle assembly relationship you must select the following elements:

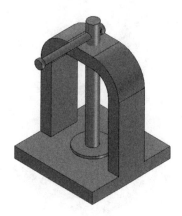

Fig. 9.9

1. Measure-To Element,
2. Measure-From Element, and
3. Measurement Plane.

These are self-explanatory.

29 Click on *Assemble* Assem...

30 Select *Angle* ⚔.

31 Select one of the planar faces of Handle as the Measure-To Element.

32 Select one of the vertical planar faces of Base as the Measure-From Element.

33 Select one of the horizontal planar faces of Base as the Measurement Plane.

Solid Edge does not always require a Measurement Plane, depending on your particular configuration and assembly relationships. When the selections for the Angle assembly relationship are complete, Solid Edge will capture the current angle between Handle and Base. To modify the angle, select the Angle assembly relationship in the bottom of the Assembly Pathfinder and you will see the Angle in the rightmost part of the ribbon bar. Type an appropriate value. It will be either 0, 90, 180, or 270 degrees. Your assembly should resemble Fig. 9.10. All the parts should be *fully positioned* ▱.

The Angle assembly relationship can be difficult to apply. As a general rule, avoid using curved surfaces, particularly cylindrical surfaces, in your selection of the measure-from and measure-to elements. Solid Edge has a couple of restrictions on the selections for the measurement planes. First, try to choose both the measure-to and measure-from elements to be normal to the measurement plane; otherwise, the message shown in Fig. 9.11 will plague you. Normally, you should have a Parallel or Axial Align assembly relationship between the parts you are placing into an Angle assembly relationship; otherwise the message in Fig. 9.12 will prevent you from completing the relationship.

9.6 Assembly Relationship Dimensions

The next objective is to modify the assembly of Fig. 9.2 to appear as shown in Fig. 9.13. This will be achieved by the use of assembly relationship dimensions. You have already seen one

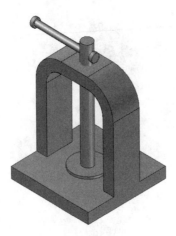

Fig. 9.10

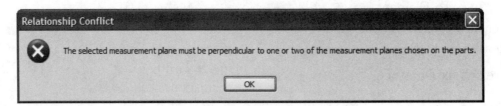

Fig. 9.11

Fig. 9.12

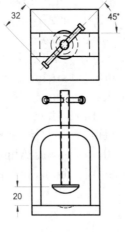

Fig. 9.13

assembly relationship dimension in the Angle assembly relationship. When you created the Angle assembly relationship, an angle dimension appeared in the Model Area. If for some reason assembly dimensions are not visible, click on the *Options* 🔲 icon on the assemble ribbon bar (get there by editing the definition of an assembly relationship). In the bottom of the dialogue box place a checkmark beside *Show all dimensions.*

There are assembly relationship dimensions, also known as Offsets, for the Mate, Planar Align, Parallel, Connect, and Tangent assembly relationships. By default they are set to zero.

| 34 | Change the angle of Handle with respect to Base. The new angle should be some multiple of 45 degrees.

| 35 | Change the offset of the Connect assembly relationship between Shaft and Base. Enter a value of *20 mm*.

The offset should be less than 32 to account for the thickness of the knob at the end of Handle and the diameter of Shaft, since the offset is measured between the faces selected in the relationship. Your assembly should resemble Fig. 9.14.

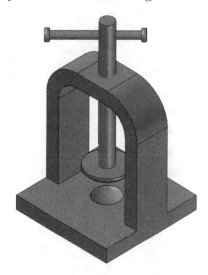

Fig. 9.14

The offsets you have modified are Fixed Offsets. They are equivalent to the driving dimensions in profiles. With fixed offsets, the designer specifies the value of the Offset. On the Assemble ribbon bar for assembly relationships, with Offset you can specify either *Fixed Offset* 🔲 or *Floating Offset* 🔁. A Floating Offset is analogous to a driven dimension. Fixed and floating assembly dimensions are coloured like driving and driven dimensions, black and blue, respectively. The value of a Floating Offset is set by another relationship. Changing from Fixed Offset to Floating Offset reduces the number of fixed DOFs by one.

Take for example the Angle assembly relationship created in Section 9.5.

| 36 | Delete the Angle Assembly relationship.

| 37 | Add a Planar Align assembly relationship between the circular end of Handle and one of the vertical planar faces of Base. When you begin creating this assembly relationship click *Floating Offset* 🔁.

Using the Floating Offset with the Planar Align assembly relationship effectively makes the Planar Align act to ensure the two selected faces are parallel where the distance between them is unfixed.

9.7   Parallel Assembly Relationship

You should become familiar with one more useful assembly relationship. The Parallel ∥ assembly relationship is very similar to the Axial Align assembly relationship, except that linear edges can be specified in addition to cylindrical faces. It enforces collinearity between the selected elements.

9.8   Summary of Assembly Relationships

A summary of the assembly relationships covered in this manual is provided in Table 9.1.

Table 9.1

Relationship	Command Icon	Indicator Icon	Max. DOFs Fixed	Rotation Locking	Offsets	Flip Side Command
Mate	▶◀	▸◂	3		✓	✓
Planar Align	▷◻	▷◼	3		✓	✓
Axial Align	▷●	▷●	4	✓		✓
Insert	⬙	▸◂ and ▷●	6	See Mate and Axial Align.		
Parallel	∥	∥	4		✓	✓
Connect	▫▪	▪	3		✓	
Angle	⦞	⦞	1		✓	
Tangent	▸ρ	▸ρ	3		✓	✓
Ground	◈ Ground	⟂	6			

9.9   Subassemblies

A **subassembly** is an assembly that is part of a greater assembly. For example, a four-cylinder engine might be a subassembly of a car. Subassemblies may have their own subassemblies as required. In Solid Edge you can add a subassembly by inserting a *.asm* file instead of a *.par* file into your assembly. A subassembly is treated as a rigid part whether or not its constituent parts are fully constrained. In the Assembly Pathfinder, you will see the *fully positioned* ⬡ icon next to subassemblies that are fully constrained within the current assembly and the *not positioned* ⬡ icon for subassemblies that are not fully constrained in the current assembly.

Exercises

1. All exercises for this chapter are located at `www.pearsoned.ca/text/fleisig`. For each exercise, download it, read it, and create a Solid Edge assembly and parts to reproduce the product in the drawings exactly. All exercises are composed of an assembly drawing, some completed parts, and detail drawings. Each assembly drawing shows a multiview projection of the assembly, exploded and/or assembled. The assembly should be fully constrained and free of interference (see Section 7.7) except between threads.

PART III

DETAIL AND ASSEMBLY DRAWINGS

CHAPTER 10

Draft Environment

Learning Objectives

After completing this chapter, you will be able to:

1. Create a new draft document.
2. Open and save draft documents.
3. Insert, reorder, delete, and rename sheets.
4. Set sheet size and background.
5. Change the viewpoint of a drawing.
6. Edit a background sheet.

Despite the wide acceptance of 3D solid modelling technology for engineering design, working drawings are still essential in manufacturing. In Solid Edge's draft environment you will learn how to create and maintain both detail and assembly drawings.

It is easy to display horizontal, frontal, and profile views in the part and assembly environments using the *Named Views* Name.. ˇ command on the main toolbar. Thus, it is not necessary to "draw" multiview drawings because Solid Edge can easily generate all the views you need: primary, auxiliary, section, exploded, etc. You will have to choose the appropriate views, annotate them with centre lines, centre marks, and dimensions and complete the title block.

The power of solid modelling technology manifests itself when parts must be modified. When manual drafting was the norm, small changes in a design could require tedious changes to many drawings. With the associative capability of Solid Edge, any change to a part will automatically be reflected in the working drawings.

This chapter will introduce you to the draft environment; in the following chapters you will learn how to create complete and correct detail and assembly drawings.

10.1 Templates

To start the draft environment you must create a new draft document. A new draft document is created in the same manner as a part or assembly document except that you must choose a draft template. All draft templates and documents have a *.dft* extension. The available draft template files are listed in Table 10.1.

Table 10.1

Template Name	Default Units	Default Dimension Style and Sheet Size
Normal.dft	Installation	Dependent
Normeng.dft	inches	ANSI
Normmet.dft	millimetres	ISO
Ansimm.dft	millimetres	ANSI

Note that *Normal.dft* is a copy of either *Normeng.dft* or *Normmet.dft*, depending on the installation options selected. The selection of template affects default units, dimension style, and available sheet sizes.

1. Create a new draft document using the *Ansimm.dft* template.

10.2 User Interface

Now that you have a new draft document open, your screen should resemble Fig. 10.1. Most of the user interface remains unchanged from the part and assembly environments. The menu bar, main toolbar, ribbon bar, and status bar are located as before, with the commands and icons somewhat altered. Notice the lack of an EdgeBar. The EdgeBar is still available but its function is not central to the draft environment. Instead, the *Sheet Tab* at the bottom left of the screen represents the first sheet in this document. It is analogous to a physical drawing sheet. You will add multiple drawings, one per sheet, to a single document. For each new sheet a new tab will appear next to *Sheet1*. When you have a large number of sheets in a document and their tabs do not all fit on the screen, use the ◄◄◄►►► icons to the left of the tabs to scroll through the sheets. You will place your views in the model area. The *Drawing View* toolbar contains the commands for creating all types of views.

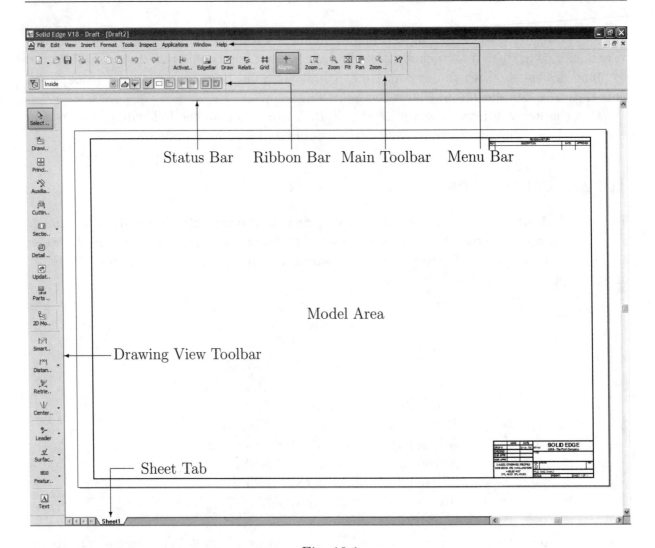

Fig. 10.1

10.3   Draft Documents

2 Open the draft document *seddb3d.dft* in *C:\Program Files\Solid Edge V18\Training* (or equivalent directory on your computer).

Your screen should resemble Fig. 10.2. Notice that there are two sheets: *Sheet1* and *Sheet2*. Click on the tabs to access the sheets one at a time.

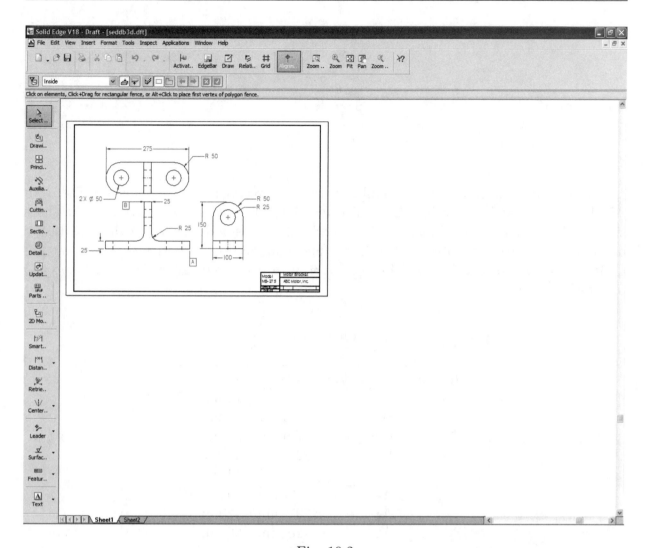

Fig. 10.2

The normal file operations such as open and save are the same for draft documents as for any other. The icon for a draft document will appear in Windows Explorer as shown in Fig. 10.3.

Draft1.dft

Fig. 10.3

10.4   Sheets

Inserting new sheets, reordering sheets, deleting sheets, and renaming sheets are easily accomplished from the context menu for a given sheet. Right-click on the tab for a given sheet and you will see the context menu shown in Fig. 10.4.

Fig. 10.4

Every sheet is given a size by default. In the example of Fig. 10.2, the sheet size is an ANSI D size in landscape orientation. The template file you choose determines the sheet sizes available, as listed in Table 10.1. The ANSI and ISO standard sheet sizes in landscape orientation are given in Table 10.2 in inches and millimetres, respectively. Note that the draft templates provided by Solid Edge only provide backgrounds for sheets in landscape orientation.

Table 10.2

Standard	Sheet Size	Height	Width
ANSI	A	$8\frac{1}{2}$ in.	11 in.
	B	11 in.	17 in.
	C	17 in.	22 in.
	D	22 in.	34 in.
	E	34 in.	44 in.
ISO	A4	210 mm	297 mm
	A3	297 mm	420 mm
	A2	420 mm	594 mm
	A1	594 mm	841 mm
	A0	841 mm	1189 mm

To change the sheet setup right-click on the sheet's tab and click on *Sheet Setup* or choose *File→Sheet Setup* from the menu bar.

3 Click on the *Background* tab of the dialogue box to get Fig. 10.5.

4 Select sheet size *A* from the *Background sheet* drop-down menu.

5 Ensure the *Show background* checkbox is checked.

The *Show background* checkbox determines whether a background is drawn. Usually you will need the background.

Selecting a suitable sheet size depends on how you intend the reader to view the drawing. If someone else is only going to view it on a computer then the only factor to consider is the detail of the drawing you are presenting. As you increase sheet size, the size of the text and thickness of lines remain the same. A large amount of detail on a small sheet size will be very difficult to read and may become cluttered. Generally, choose the smallest size sheet that will be easy to read. You can always change your sheet size later when creating and

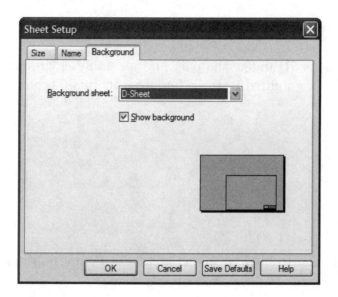

Fig. 10.5

annotating your views. If you are printing your drawings, you must ensure that you have the appropriate output device to handle larger sheets. Normally, office laser printers can handle ANSI A- and B-size sheets but larger sheet sizes require a plotter. When printing or plotting your drawing, it must be printed to scale, or "not to scale" (NTS) must be clearly indicated. For example, if you print a C-size drawing on an A-size sheet of paper, you must indicate "NTS."

10.5 Background Sheets

The default background sheets include a title block, revision block, and border. These can easily be modified to suit the needs of your organization. Display the background sheets by clicking on *View→Background Sheets* on the menu bar. The background sheets will appear as additional sheets in your draft document. To hide them click the same menu item again. To edit them use the tools on the *Drawing* toolbar (Fig. 10.6). If you cannot see this toolbar, then right-click on any visible toolbar and select *Drawing* or click *Draw* Draw in the main toolbar.

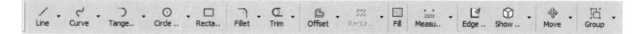

Fig. 10.6

10.6 Viewing

The draft environment is 2D unlike the part and assembly environments. The commands for changing your view are limited to those found on the main toolbar:

1. *Zoom Area* Zoom...,

2. *Zoom* Zoom,

3. *Fit* Fit,

4. *Pan* Pan, and

5. *Zoom Tool* Zoom...

Click on the Fit command to fill your model area with the current drawing.

CHAPTER 11

Detail Drawings

Learning Objectives

After completing this chapter, you will be able to:

1. Create detail drawings.
2. Select and place primary views in a detail drawing.
3. Create additional primary views.
4. Create auxiliary, section, and detail views.
5. Add centre marks and lines.
6. Dimension a detail drawing.
7. Add annotations and text.

The job of creating a detail drawing from the solid model of a part is, in general, an easy task. Your primary concern will be learning the commands available for this task, and making decisions with regard to view selection and dimensioning. The basic workflow for creating a detail drawing is:

1. Choose a drawing convention (ANSI or ISO) and standard sheet sizes.
2. Create a sheet and choose a sheet size.
3. Choose a part.
4. Select a front view.
5. Select other primary views.
6. Place primary views.
7. Add additional views if necessary.
8. Add centre marks and lines.
9. Dimension.
10. Annotate.
11. Fill in the title block.
12. Indicate scale.

At the end of this chapter are several exercises where you will be asked to create a fully dimensioned detail drawing following a particular engineering drawing convention.

In preparation for the remainder of this chapter, take a look at the part *anchor.par* in *C:\Program Files\Solid Edge V18\Training* (or equivalent directory on your computer). The part is shown in Fig. 11.1. It will be used to demonstrate how to create a detail drawing. To begin, do the following:

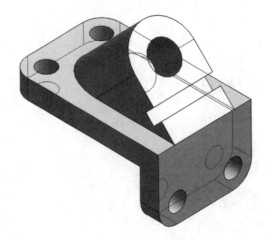

Fig. 11.1

1. Create a new draft document based on the template *Ansimm.dft*.
2. Set the sheet size to *C*.

11.1   Part Selection and Primary Views

Now you will select your part and primary views, and place them on the sheet.

3. Click on *Fit* Fit.
4. Click on *Drawing View Creation Wizard* Drawi...

You will see the dialogue box in Fig. 11.2. You are being prompted to select the Solid Edge part from which the detail drawing views will be generated.

5. Select Anchor (*anchor.par*) and click on *Open*.

This will move you to the next step in the wizard, shown in Fig. 11.3. Normally, settings on this page will not need to be changed.

6. Click on *Next* at the bottom to go to the next step.

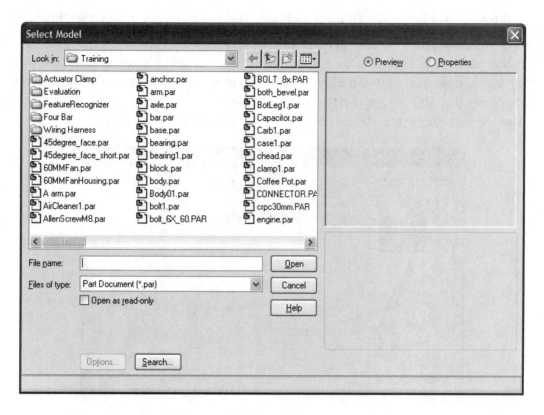

Fig. 11.2

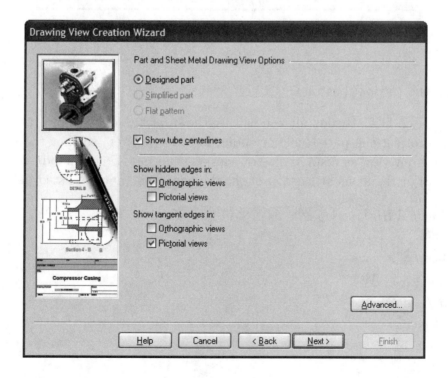

Fig. 11.3

Now you will see Fig. 11.4. You must choose the front, or frontal, view. The displayed items *front*, *right*, *top*, and *iso* are taken from the Named Views Name.. ˙ stored with the design model in the part's file. It will often be the case that you will choose one of these views as your front view. However, you can also use the *Custom view* option. Note that if you select *iso*, you will not be able to go to the *Next* step. For Anchor, the *front* option is a good choice. However, to illustrate the use of the *Custom* option you will try it.

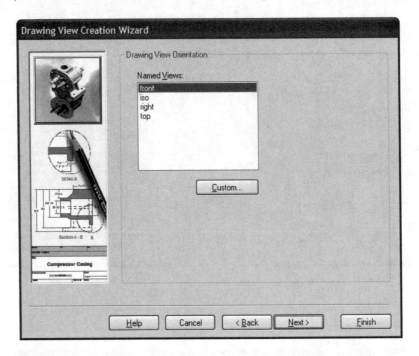

Fig. 11.4

7 Click on the *Custom* button.

You will see Fig. 11.5. By default you will see the *front* named view of your part. Use this dialogue box to orient the part (scale or zoom does not matter) so that the view you wish to use as your front view is displayed. You can use the mouse commands you are familiar with (Table 2.2) or the icons at the top of the dialogue box that are listed below:

- *Shaded with VHL Overlay*
- *Rotate*
- *Spin About*
- *Common Views*
- *Look at Face*
- *Align Edge*
- *Zoom Area*
- *Zoom*
- *Fit*
- *Pan*

Fig. 11.5

All these commands are used to change the view of your part. Most of them involve using your mouse to adjust the orientation of the part. Manual adjustment will orient your part close to, but not exactly in, the desired orientation. Consequently, the faces you want to make parallel to the screen will be slightly out of alignment and when you add dimensions they will be wrong. Study Fig. 11.6. Fig. 11.6(a) is correctly aligned and Fig. 11.6(b) is poorly aligned. Notice that in Fig. 11.6(b) the hidden lines should not be there. To avoid this problem you need to make the alignment exact. Use the *Look at Face* or *Common Views* commands to "snap" the orientation of the part to an exact alignment. Use the *Look at Face* command to make a specified face parallel to the screen or use the *Common Views* command to select an orientation parallel to one of the cardinal reference planes.

8 Click on *Rotate* to change the orientation of the part a little bit.

9 Select a face parallel to the front named view using the *Look At Face* command to return it to its original orientation.

10 Click on *Close*.

Your screen should now look like Fig. 11.7. Here you will select the primary views you wish to have in addition to the front view. Note that the icon in the middle is already depressed. It denotes the front view you just selected. It cannot be unselected. It is obligatory.

11 Depress the *Top View* icon directly above the front view icon.

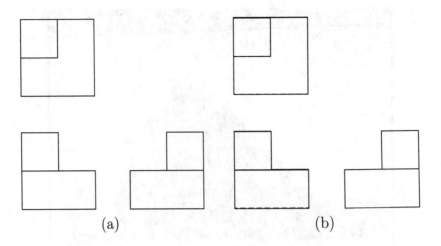

(a)   (b)

Fig. 11.6

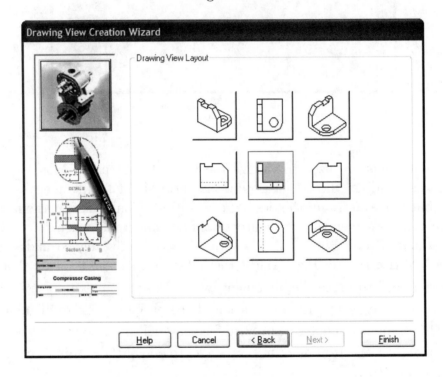

Fig. 11.7

Do not select the *Right Side View* icon because you will add it after you have completed using the drawing view creation wizard.

☐12 Click on *Finish*.

The last step in the drawing view creation wizard is to select a location for the two primary views you have selected. As you move your mouse pointer over the model, a silhouette of the two views in the shape of a tall rectangle will follow the cursor.

☐13 Click in the model area to place the views.

Select a location so the views are in the middle of the drawing and are not overlapping the border or title block. Your screen should resemble Fig. 11.8.

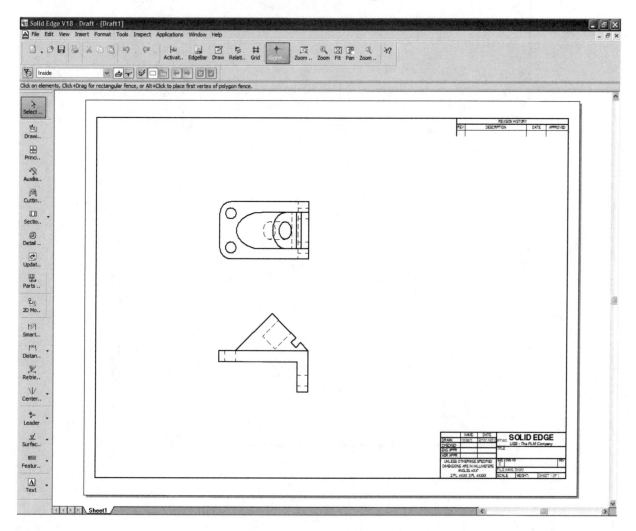

Fig. 11.8

If you have placed the views in the wrong place you can easily move them around by selecting a view and then dragging it with your mouse pointer.

Notice that Solid Edge has automatically chosen a scale for your views to fit comfortably in the current sheet. The scale of your views can be changed by selecting a primary view and then clicking on *Properties* in the ribbon bar. A dialogue box will appear. Select the *General* tab. You will see Fig. 11.9. The scale can be adjusted under *View Scale*.

11.2   Additional Views

The next step in the draft environment workflow is adding additional views if necessary. You must decide which views are necessary.

Earlier, you omitted the right-side view. Now add it.

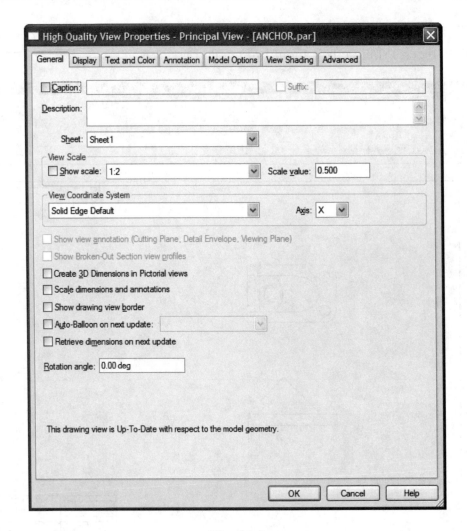

Fig. 11.9

14 Click on *Principal View* Princi...

15 Click on the front view and move your mouse pointer to the right.

A silhouette of the right-side view will appear.

16 Click to place the view.

Your drawing should resemble Fig. 11.10. With the Principal View command you can add a primary view adjacent to any existing primary view.
   Now you will add an auxiliary view.

17 Click on *Auxiliary View* Auxilia...

18 Move your mouse pointer over the front view until the "folding line" shown in Fig. 11.11 appears.

19 Click and then move your mouse pointer to the upper right of your drawing to place the auxiliary view.

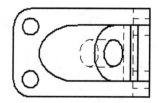

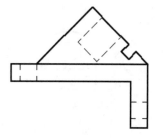

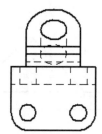

Fig. 11.10

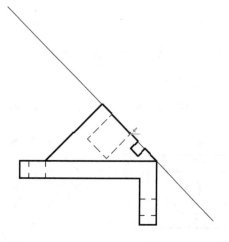

Fig. 11.11

Your drawing should appear as shown in Fig. 11.12.

In general, auxiliary views can be created either parallel to an existing element, as demonstrated above, or perpendicular. Switch between the two options by selecting the commands *Parallel* ⬚ and *Perpendicular* ⬚, respectively, on the auxiliary view ribbon bar.

Remove the folding line and labels (Fig. 11.12) created by Solid Edge for the auxiliary view.

20 Select the auxiliary view.
21 Right-click on it.
22 Click on *Properties*.
23 Click on *General*.

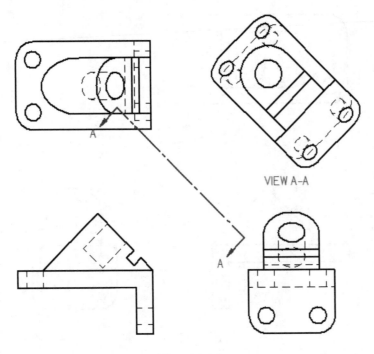

Fig. 11.12

24 Uncheck *Caption*, *Suffix*, and *Show view annotation*.
25 Click on *OK*.

Your drawing should be "cleaned up" as shown in Fig. 11.13.

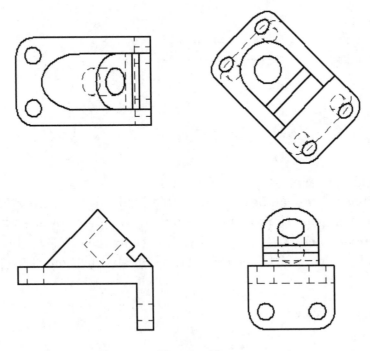

Fig. 11.13

The anchor part does not demand a section view because the part has no hidden features.

To demonstrate a section view you will create one. A section view involves two steps. First you create a cutting plane and then you create a section view based on the cutting plane.

26 Click on *Cutting Plane* Cuttin...

27 Click on the right view because this is where you will place your cutting plane.

Solid Edge will pause for a moment and your toolbars will change. The *Drawing Views* toolbar will be replaced with the *Drawing* toolbar. The commands on the Drawing toolbar should be familiar to you. They are similar to ones available when drawing profiles.

28 Click on *Line* Line if it is not already selected.

29 Create an offset cutting plane as shown in Fig. 11.14. Make sure you click on key points to get your cutting plane line placed exactly. Use relationships where necessary.

30 Click on *Finish* when the line is complete.

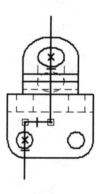

Fig. 11.14

This will return your original toolbars and then you will have to click once more to select the direction in which the arrows point.

31 Click to select the direction shown in Fig. 11.15.

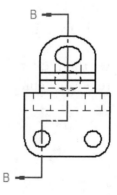

Fig. 11.15

The cutting plane "line" does not have to be a single line. To create an offset section or revolved section you will have to use more than one line. These will have to be joined with connect relationships. Note that normally if you plan to leave the cutting plane line visible, it should extend beyond the view of the part such that the arrowheads and labels are not superimposed on the view but are next to the view, with a bit of space between them.

| 32 | Start the *Section View* Sectio.. command. |

| 33 | Select the cutting plane you just created. |

If you were creating a revolved section view then you would click on the *Revolved Section View* icon located on the ribbon bar.

| 34 | Click to place the section view as shown in Fig. 11.16. |

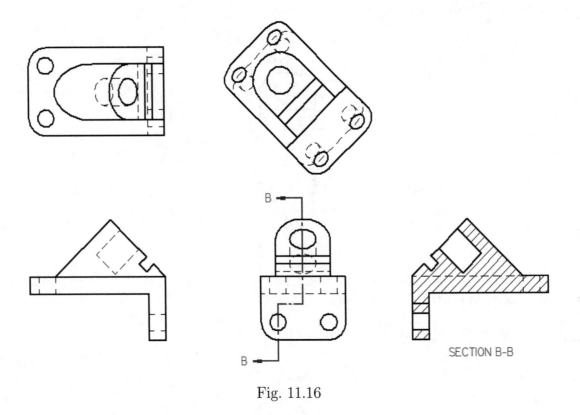

Fig. 11.16

Notice that by default Solid Edge draws the hidden lines in a section view. Since this does not conform to convention, you must remove them.

| 35 | Click on *Select Tool* Select... |

| 36 | Select the section view. |

| 37 | Right-click on the section view. |

| 38 | Click on *Properties*. |

| 39 | In the dialogue box on the *Display* tab uncheck *Hidden edge style*. |

| 40 | You will see Fig. 11.17. Click on *OK*. |

Fig. 11.17

41 Click on *OK*.

Both revolved and offset section views suffer from the same problem. Fig. 11.18(a) illustrates a correct and conventional offset section view. Fig. 11.18(b) illustrates an offset section view with edges placed where the section line changes direction. These should be removed. However, to do so you must convert the section view to a **draft view**. Essentially, this means removing the associativity of the view with the part so that if the part changes, the view will no longer be updated. This is necessary so that you can modify the projection in a non-standard way.

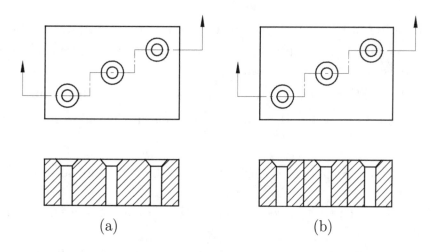

(a)   (b)

Fig. 11.18

42 Select the section view.

43 Right-click over the section view.

44 Select *Convert to 2D View*.

45 Click on *Yes* in the dialogue box (Fig. 11.19).

46 Right-click over the section view again, then select *Draw in View* from the menu.

47 Remove the line that should not appear in the section view: select it and delete it. When removed your section view should appear like the one in Fig. 11.20.

48 Click on *Return* to exit the command.

Solid Edge directly supports full, offset, revolved, and broken section views. Other types of section views, such as half and removed section, can be created by manually drawing them

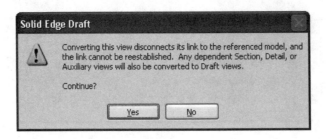

Fig. 11.19

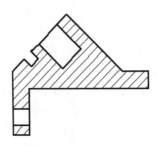

Fig. 11.20

or using a combination of tools. Use *Section Only* ▦ to draw only the section and *Modify Drawing View Boundary* ▣ to clip a view. Combine multiple views and draw additional edges using the tools on the Drawing toolbar.

The *Broken-Out Section View* Broke.. command (found on the flyout underneath *Section View* Sectio..) modifies a view rather than adds a new one in the following SmartStep ribbon bar steps.

1. *Select Source View Step* ▦ — Select the view that will be the source of the broken section.
2. *Profile Step* ▣ — Draw a closed profile in the view for the area that is going to be broken out.
3. *Depth Step* ▧ — Select the depth of the broken-out section by either typing in a depth value in the ribbon bar or clicking in an adjacent primary view.
4. *Select Target View Step* ▦ — Select the view where the broken-out section will be placed. This is usually the same as in the first step.

Finally, a detail view is used to show some detail of a given view at a different scale to add clarity. Use the *Detail View* Detail.. command to create a detail view. A detail view in Solid Edge is a circular portion of an existing view in your drawing that magnifies some detail.

49 Click on *Detail View* Detail...
50 Click to locate the centre of the area to be magnified, as displayed in the front view in Fig. 11.21.
51 Click again to specify the radius of the area to be magnified.

52 Click to place the new view.

Your sheet should look something like Fig. 11.21.

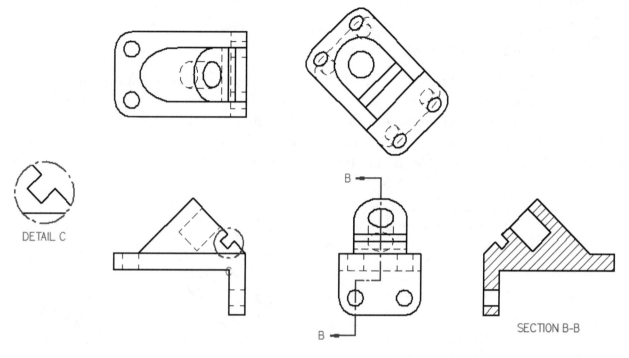

DETAIL C

B

B

SECTION B-B

Fig. 11.21

As you are working, you will notice that you may not have sufficient space within the borders of your sheet to place all the views. Use the properties dialogue box for a primary view to adjust the scale as needed. All adjacent primary and other views will automatically change scale too. Alternatively, change the size of your sheet. When you find you do not need a view, simply select it and press the *Delete* key. Note that all dependent views will be deleted too.

11.3   Centre Lines and Centre Marks

The next step in creating a draft file is to add centre lines and marks. You will have to be familiar with the dimensioning convention to determine when and where these are necessary. Solid Edge provides commands for manually placing centre lines, centre marks, and bolt hole circles, as well as commands for automatically adding centre lines and centre marks.

Begin by adding the centre lines and marks automatically.

53 Click on *Automatic Center Lines* Autom... It is found in the flyout revealed by clicking on *Center Line* Center...

In the ribbon bar you will see a number of icons.

[54] Ensure that *Centre Lines* ⬇️, *Centre Marks* ⊕, *Center Mark Projection Lines* ✛, and *Connect Center Marks* ⬚ are depressed.

This will ensure that these elements are added to the views.

[55] Ensure that *Add Lines and Marks* ⊞ is also depressed.

[56] Click on each view in turn.

Your sheet should resemble Fig. 11.22. Any necessary additional fine tuning can be done by clicking on *Center Line and Center Mark Options* ▦ on the ribbon bar and making the appropriate changes. To remove the automatic centre lines, select *Remove Lines and Marks* ✖ on the ribbon bar and select the views from which you wish to remove the centre lines, marks, and projection lines created by the automatic command.

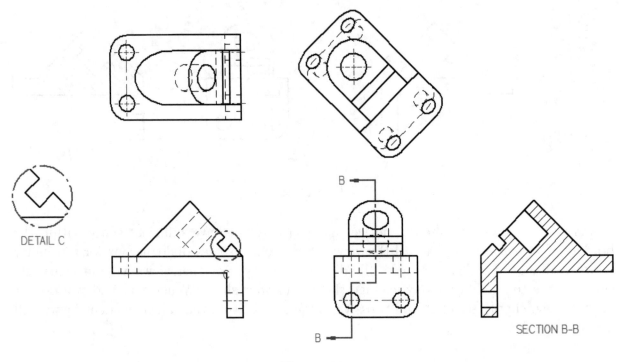

Fig. 11.22

Examine the auxiliary view in Fig. 11.22. Notice that the centre mark and its projection lines are oriented in a normal fashion. They should be corrected by tilting them to the angle of the view.

[57] Click on *Select Tool* Select...

[58] Select the centre mark in the auxiliary view and its projection lines.

[59] Delete them by pressing the *Delete* key.

You will add a centre mark in the correct orientation manually.

[60] Click on *Center Mark* Center... It is found in the flyout revealed by clicking on *Center Line* Center...

[61] Ensure that *Projection Lines* ⊕ on the ribbon bar is depressed to get centre mark projection lines.

Next, you must select the orientation of the centre mark using the *Orientation* drop-down menu on the ribbon bar. The options are:

1. *Horizontal/Vertical* — The default places the centre mark in the normal orientation.
2. *Use Dimension Axis* — Use the *Dimension Axis* ⬚ command to select a direction first and the subsequent placement of a centre mark will follow this orientation.
3. *By 2 Points* — Use this to select the orientation using two points.

[62] Click on *Use Dimension Axis* from the *Center Mark — Orientation* pull-down menu on the ribbon bar.
[63] Click on *Dimension Axis* ⬚ on the ribbon bar.
[64] Click on any of the angled object lines in the auxiliary view.
[65] Click on the hole in the auxiliary view.

A centre mark can be placed on a midpoint or an endpoint of a line, on a point, or on the centre of an arc.

The centre line on the inclined hole is missing in the section view.

[66] Click on *Center Line* Center...

Examine the *Placement Options* drop-down menu on the ribbon bar. You will have two options to place centre lines: *By 2 Points* and *By 2 Lines*. When placing *By 2 Points*, select two points and a centre line will be drawn between them. When placing *By 2 Lines* the centre line will be drawn at an equal distance from both selected lines. Use this command to draw not only centre lines, but also axes of symmetry and centre connection lines. Sometimes you will find that the centre line is too short. To move the ends, just select the centre line with *Select Tool* Select.. and drag the black boxes at the ends of the line.

[67] Place a centre line in the section view as shown in Fig. 11.23.

Bolt Hole Circle Bolt H.. is a rarely used, but useful, command for creating bolt hole circles, centre marks, and centre mark projection lines as shown in Fig. 11.24.

11.4   Dimensions

The following step is the addition of dimensions to your drawing. It is up to you to determine how many and which dimensions are needed. Solid Edge merely provides you with the tools needed to add and edit dimensions on a drawing.

[68] Click on *Retrieve Dimension* Retrie...

This command adds dimensions to your drawing from the part's features — the kind that you would see when selecting the *Show Dimensions* command for a feature.

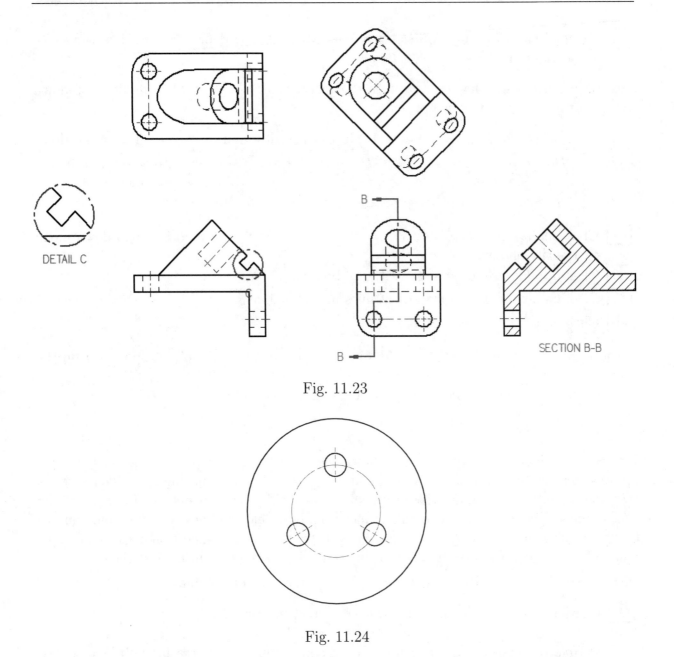

Fig. 11.23

Fig. 11.24

69 Select each view in turn.

Notice that you cannot select the auxiliary or detail views. When done, your drawing should appear as shown in Fig. 11.25. Notice that this command, while useful, does not add all the necessary dimensions and some added dimensions require editing. One frequent problem is the lack of visible gaps between the extension lines and the projection. Fig. 11.26 shows another example of a visible gap problem: the extension line on the left displays a correct gap and the extension line on the right is missing the gap altogether, which is unacceptable. To see the section view more clearly, right-click on the section and select *Fit Drawing View* from the context menu.

Solid Edge provides a number of dimensioning tools that should be familiar from the part environment when you created profiles. These will be examined in turn. You will add

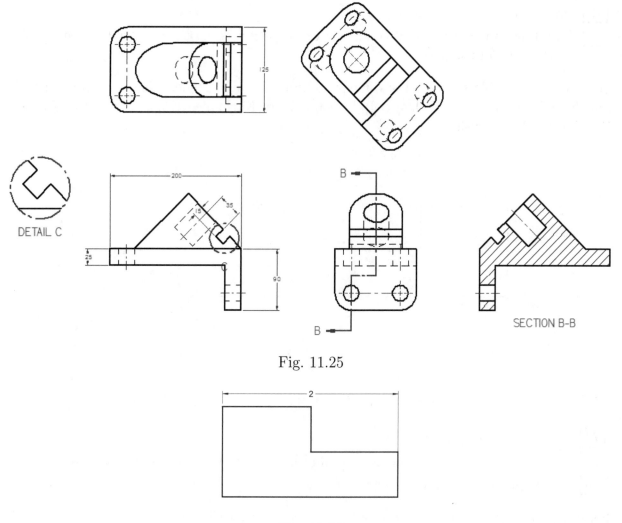

Fig. 11.25

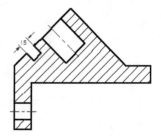

Fig. 11.26

dimensions to the section with the appropriate visible gaps.

70　Click on *SmartDimension* Smart...

71　Select the single line at the bottom of the notch and place the dimension.

Notice that you are missing the visible gap as shown in Fig. 11.27.

Fig. 11.27

72 Delete the dimension again.

73 Add it again using the same command but this time select the parallel lines that make up the sides of the notch.

You will not be able to place the dimension at the desired angle. This is a limitation of the *SmartDimension* tool. This tool also cannot create chained (Fig. 11.28(a)) or stacked (Fig. 11.28(b)) dimensions.

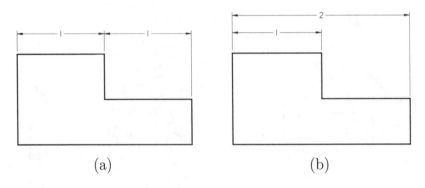

(a)   (b)

Fig. 11.28

To add any but the simplest linear dimensions use the *Distance Between* Distan.. command.

74 Click on *Distance Between* Distan...

75 Select *By 2 Points* from the *Orientation* drop-down menu on the ribbon bar.

76 Select the points at the top of the notch.

Selecting edges or midpoints will usually lead to missing visible gaps.

77 Click to place the dimension.

78 Click on *Distance Between* Distan...

79 Click on the 15 dimension you just created.

80 Click on the endpoint of the centre line in the section view.

81 Click to place the dimension.

Depending on where you clicked to place the dimension, you will either get a stacked or chained dimension. Your section view will resemble Fig. 11.29. Notice that the arrows on the 15 dimension are pointing "in." A dimension can be toggled from "in" to "out" by selecting the arrowhead and dragging it across the extension line. It helps to zoom in on the arrowhead first.

Add a diameter dimension for one of the holes using the SmartDimension command in the top view.

82 Zoom in on the horizontal (top) view of the drawing.

83 Click on *SmartDimension* Smart...

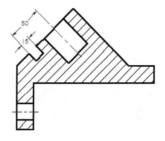

Fig. 11.29

84 Dimension one of the diameter 24 holes in the horizontal view.

85 Click on *Select Tool* Select ...

86 Select the dimension you just created.

87 Click on *Prefix* 📝 in the ribbon bar.

You will see the dialogue box shown in Fig. 11.30.

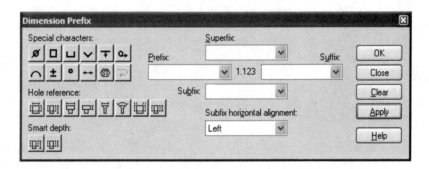

Fig. 11.30

88 Type *2X* in the *Prefix* box.

89 Click on *OK*.

Your horizontal view should resemble Fig. 11.31.

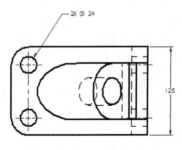

Fig. 11.31

The Angle Between Angle .. command allows you to create stacked and chained dimensions for angles in the same manner as with *Dimension Between*. The *Coordinate Dimension* Coordi..

and *Angular Coordinate Dimension* Angula.. commands allow you to create both linear and angular dimensions, respectively.

For outside diameters, Solid Edge provides *Symmetric Diameter* Symm... Select a centre line and a point on the part to dimension it. The *Half/Full* icon on the ribbon bar determines whether the dimension appears as Fig. 11.32(a) or Fig. 11.32(b).

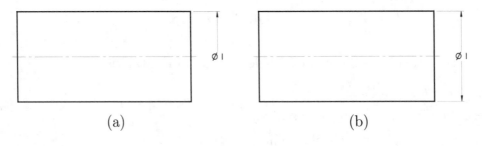

(a)   (b)

Fig. 11.32

Finally, you can dimension chamfers using the *Chamfer Dimension* Chamf.. command. The steps are:

1. Select a baseline.
2. Select a measure line.
3. Click to place the dimension.

Orientation can be selected *along axis*, *callout perpendicular*, or *callout parallel*.

11.5   Annotations

In the last step in the draft environment workflow you must add annotations. How to add text and callouts will be explained.

Adding text is a simple task. Use the *Text* Text command to add text to your title block. Zoom in on the title block using the *Zoom Area* Zoom.. command. Just click to place the text and type. Use this also to indicate the scale of your sheet in the title block. You will find the scale of your sheet on the *General* tab of the properties dialogue box of any primary view. Text can be placed anywhere on the sheet.

90 Add a name for the drawing in the title block.

91 Indicate the scale of the drawing in the title block.

Callouts like the one in Fig. 11.33 provide several pieces of information. Use the *Callout* Callout command (found on the flyout underneath the *Leader* Leader icon) to create them. When you start the command, the dialogue box shown in Fig. 11.34 will immediately appear. In the *Callout text* field place the text you wish to see. There are escape sequences for special characters such as diameter, depth, degree, etc. The *%HC* escape sequence refers to *Hole* *callout.* This means if your callout points to a *Hole* or *Thread* feature, Solid Edge will extract the parameters from said feature and display them in the callout. That is how the text for the counterbore hole in Fig. 11.33 was generated. Alternatively, you can choose to enter the text manually. The first line in the *Callout text* field would be *%DI 10 THRU* and the second line *%CB %DI 12 %DP 9*. Once you are satisfied with the text, click on *OK* and place your callout. You may also wish to select the icons *Leader* and *Break Line* in the ribbon bar to add a leader and break line to that leader.

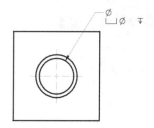

Fig. 11.33

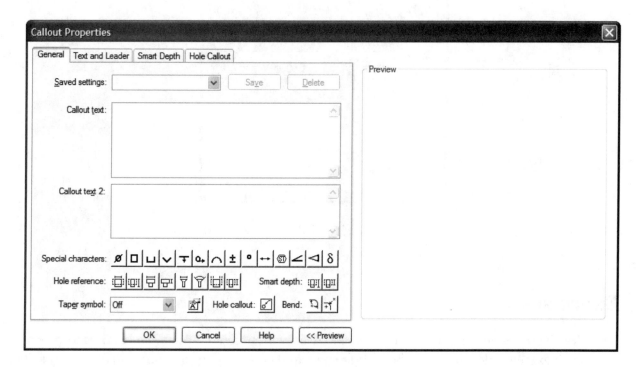

Fig. 11.34

11.6 Editing and Updating Parts

Associativity means that changes to a part will be reflected by changes in the draft file. To change a part double-click a view of it. This will open the part file. Once the changes have been made, you will have to use the *Tools→Drawing View Tracker* command on the menu bar in the draft environment (Fig. 11.35). Click on *Update Views* 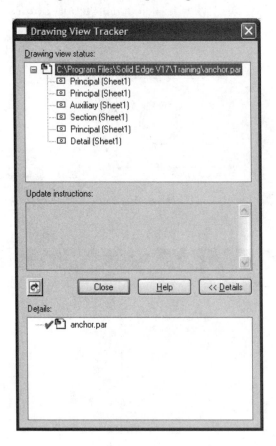 and then on *OK*. You may additionally have to update individual views by clicking on *Update View* in the context menu of each view. Changes to a part may break some views, dimensions, and centre lines/marks. These problems, flagged by numbers within a triangle, must be corrected manually by deleting the offending item and replacing it.

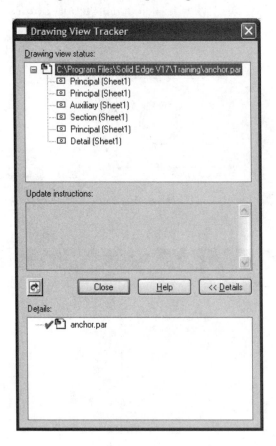

Fig. 11.35

Exercises

1. All exercises for this chapter are located at `www.pearsoned.ca/text/fleisig`. For each exercise, download the Solid Edge part and create a complete and correct Solid Edge detail drawing to communicate the size and shape of the part. The drawing must conform to conventions followed in your locale.

CHAPTER 12

Assembly Drawings

Learning Objectives

After completing this chapter, you will be able to:

1. Create exploded display configurations.
2. Place exploded assembly views in a draft file.
3. Edit flow lines.
4. Add a bill of materials to an assembly drawing.
5. Create assembly drawings.

The workflow for creating exploded assembly drawings requires two steps. First, you will explode the assembly and save the result in a configuration file. Then, you will place the view on the sheet of a draft file, add a bill of materials, dimensions, and annotations.

At the end of this chapter are several exercises where you will be asked to create exploded assembly drawings following a particular engineering drawing convention.

For the purposes of this chapter, you will use the training assembly *trolley.asm* located in *C:\Program Files\Solid Edge V18\Training* (or equivalent directory on your computer). This assembly is shown in Fig. 12.1(a). It has several parts and instances of two different assemblies as shown in Fig. 12.1(b). You may have to make a copy of *trolley.asm*, its part files, and subassembly files if you cannot write to the directory where they are stored.

12.1   Exploded View Environment

1. Open *trolley.asm*.
2. Click on *Applications→Exploded View* in the menu bar.

This will take you into a new environment with a new toolbar: *Exploded View*. You will use the various commands on this toolbar to "explode" your assembly. When creating an exploded view, Solid Edge will ignore the assembly relationships to separate the parts, but assembly relationships will be used to constrain the placement of exploded parts. Like other environments, this one has its own document type. The configuration of parts is saved by Solid Edge in a **display configuration**. You can have multiple display configurations

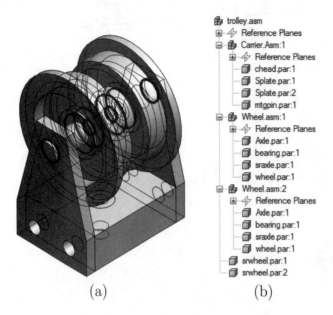

(a)   (b)

Fig. 12.1

associated with any assembly. One or more display configurations is stored in a configuration file with the extension *.cfg*. Each display configuration in a configuration file stores the relative positions and orientations of the part plus the current point of view and zoom of the view. This is important because when you go to create your assembly drawing, unlike with detail drawings, you will not be able to choose among views. The view will be taken from the display configuration you choose. The current display configuration is saved when you exit the exploded view environment or when you manually save, using the *Tools→Configuration→Display Configurations* (Fig. 12.2) command on the menu bar.

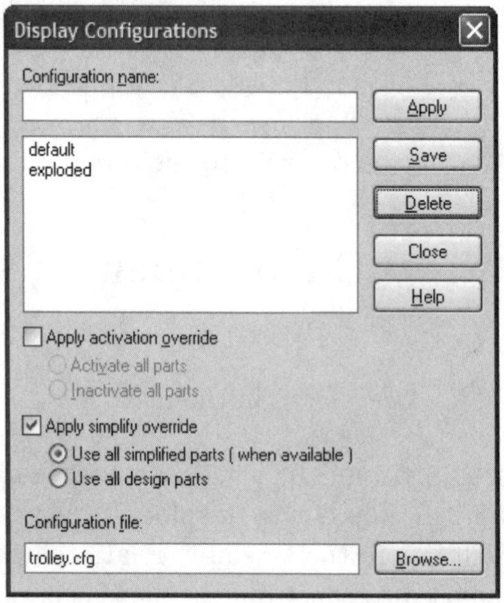

Fig. 12.2

The following commands for creating and editing exploded assemblies are found on the *Exploded View* toolbar in the exploded view environment.

- *Automatic Explode* Autom.. — Automatically explode the entire assembly.

- *Explode* Explode — Sometimes the automatic explode command creates unwanted or unexpected results. Explode part or all of your assembly manually with this command.

- *Adjust Spread Distance* Adjust.. — Increase or decrease the distance between exploded parts.

- *Reposition* Repos.. — Reorder exploded parts.

- *Remove* Remove — Remove a part from the explosion and hide it.

- *Collapse* Collap.. — Unexplode one or more parts.

- *Add Joggle* Add Jo.. — Add a joggle to a flow line.

- *Remove Joggle* Remo.. — Remove a joggle from a flow line.

- *Unexplode* Unexp.. — Unexplode the entire assembly to start over again.

- *Bind Subassembly* Bind S.. — Cause a subassembly to be treated as a part; that is, do not explode the parts within a subassembly.

- *Unbind Subassembly* Unbin.. — Explode all parts in a subassembly.

Now explode the assembly.

3 Click on *Automatic Explode* Autom...

4 Click on the *Explode* button on the ribbon bar.

5 Click on the small black triangle to the right of the *Named Views* Name.. ˙ icon and select *right*.

6 If your assembly disappears, click on *Fit* Fit. Your screen should resemble Fig. 12.3.

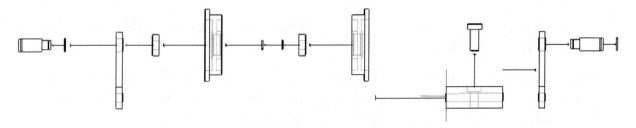

Fig. 12.3

7 Click on *Reposition* Repos...

8 Click on *wheel.par:1* in subassembly *Wheel.asm:2* (highlighted in Fig. 12.4).

9 Click on *Splate.par:1* in subassembly *Carrier.Asm:1* (highlighted in Fig. 12.5). Your assembly should now resemble Fig. 12.6.

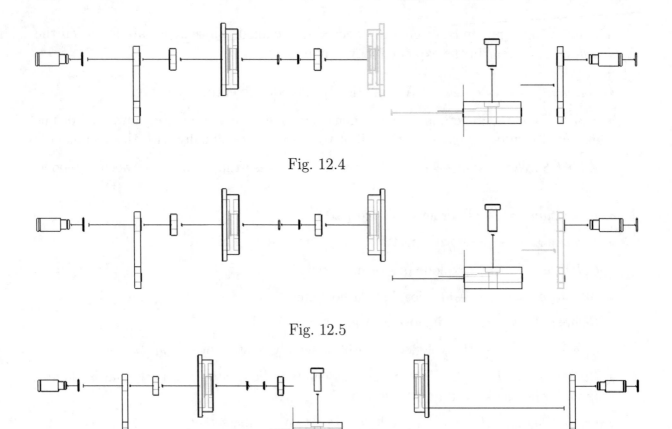

Fig. 12.4

Fig. 12.5

Fig. 12.6

10   Switch back to the isometric view.

11   Use the Fit command if necessary.

Chances are that some parts will appear overlapped.

12   Click on *Adjust Spread Distance* Adjust...

13   Select the parts and drag them so that some background appears between each pair of parts, as shown in Fig. 12.7.

In this command, it is sometimes easier to move more than one part (*Single Part* [ ] on the ribbon bar) at a time. Select *Part Plus Dependents* [ ] from the ribbon bar to adjust the spread distance of a given part and its dependents together at the same time.

     Return to the assembly environment.

14   Click on *Select Tool* Select...

15   Click on *Return* in the ribbon bar.

16   Click on *File→Save As* from the menu bar. Save the assembly to the *Desktop*.

Solid Edge has saved your exploded configuration in the *trolley.cfg* file with the name *explode,loginname* where *loginname* is the user name with which you logged in.

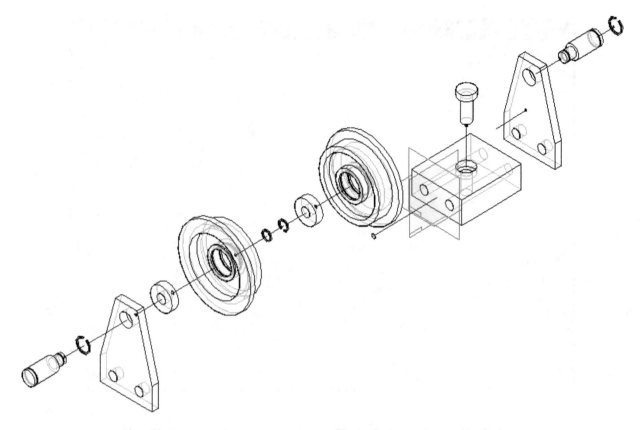

Fig. 12.7

12.2   Draft Environment

With the exploded view display configuration ready, you can create an assembly drawing.

[17] Open a new draft file based on the *Ansimm.dft* template file.

[18] Set the sheet size to *C*.

[19] Click on *Fit* [Fit].

   You will select the assembly, place the view, edit flow lines, and add a bill of materials.

[20] Click on *Drawing View Wizard* [Drawi...].

[21] When prompted to select a model, select *Assembly Document (*.asm)* from *Files of type*. See Fig. 12.8(a).

[22] Select *trolley.asm* and click on *Open*.

Then you will see the dialogue presented in Fig. 12.8(b).

[23] In the *Configuration* drop-down menu, select your *explode,loginname* display configuration.

[24] Click on *Finish*.

[25] Click in the drawing to place your exploded assembly view.

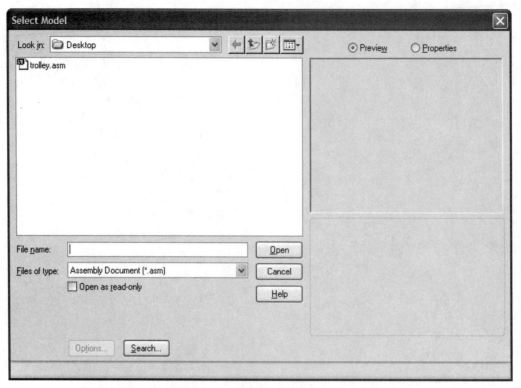

(a)

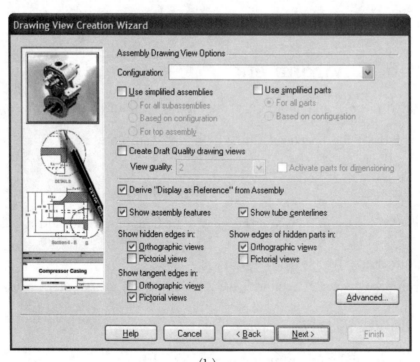

(b)

Fig. 12.8

If your view appears small compared to the borders of the drawing, adjust the scale of the view to fill the space but not overlap the borders. Your drawing should resemble Fig. 12.9.

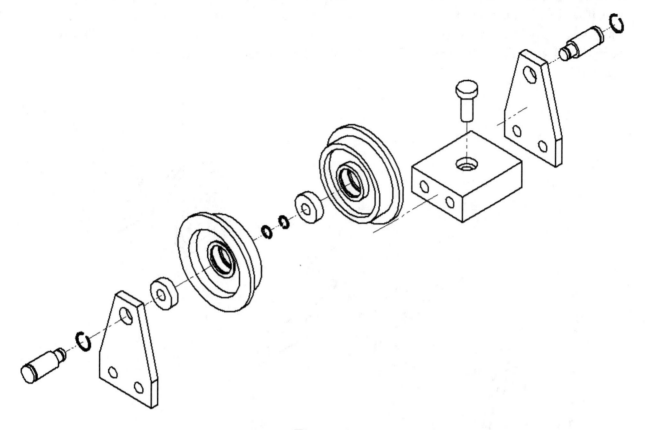

Fig. 12.9

The default flow lines are not ideal. Solid Edge provides a crude method for adding the flow lines you wish to see but, unfortunately, removing offending flow lines has a catch. Edit the flow lines.

26   Select the exploded view.

27   Right-click on the exploded view.

28   Select *Draw in View* from the context menu.

29   Select a flow line.

30   Press the *Delete* key.

You cannot delete just one flow line, you must delete them all. Add back the flow lines manually.

31   Use the Line ʟⁱⁿᵉ command to add back the flow lines you need.

32   Choose *Phantom* on the ribbon bar of the line command.

33   Draw the needed flow lines in the view.

34   Use the Trim ᵀʳⁱᵐ command to remove portions of unneeded flow lines.

[35] Click on *Return* in the ribbon bar.

When complete, your flow lines should appear as shown in Fig. 12.10. Note that by deleting the flow lines automatically created by Solid Edge and adding your own manually, you have lost associativity between the assembly view and the assembly. If the assembly view is updated to reflect changes in the assembly, Solid Edge will add back the flow lines you deleted.

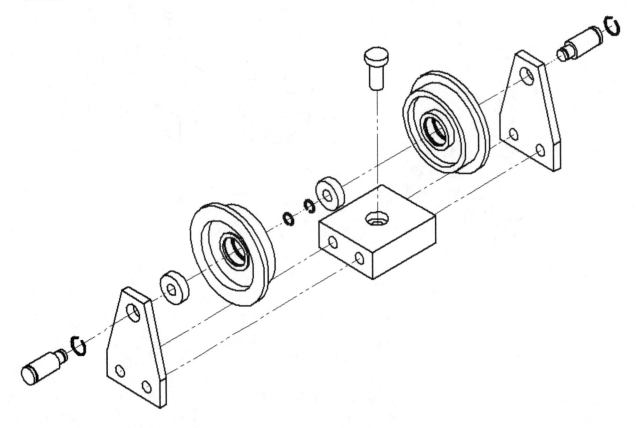

Fig. 12.10

The last new step is adding a bill of materials (BOM) or parts list in the terminology used by Solid Edge.

[36] Click on *Parts List* Parts...

[37] In the ribbon bar, ensure that *Auto-Balloon* and *Place List* are depressed.

These options place the balloons identifying individual parts and the parts list on the drawing when you complete the command.

[38] Click on the view to select it.

[39] Click on *Properties* in the ribbon bar.

[40] In the *Columns* tab, make the selections shown in Fig. 12.11(a).

These selections determine which columns will appear in the parts list on the drawing. For this example, only a minimal set of information is needed. Note that to set the *Title* of a

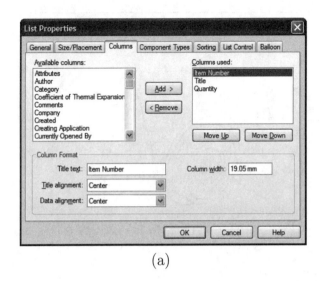
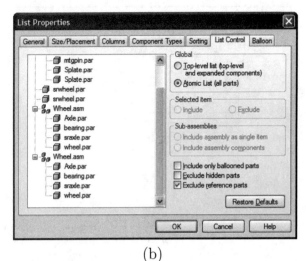

(a)   (b)

Fig. 12.11

part or subassembly, go to *File→File Properties→Summary* in the menu bar when editing a part or assembly.

41 Go to the *List Control* tab and select *Atomic List (all parts)*.

This will cause Solid Edge to list all the parts, including the ones in subassemblies, as separate items in the parts list; otherwise, Solid Edge will list each subassembly as an item but not its constituent parts.

42 Click on *OK*.

43 Click on *Finish*.

Balloons and the parts list will be placed on your drawing.

44 Use your mouse pointer to drag the balloons and the parts list until they do not intersect the view or the border of the drawing.

Your drawing should resemble Fig. 12.12.

The last step to completing an assembly drawing is to apply dimensions and annotations, if necessary, including filling in the title block. Use the commands described in the previous chapter.

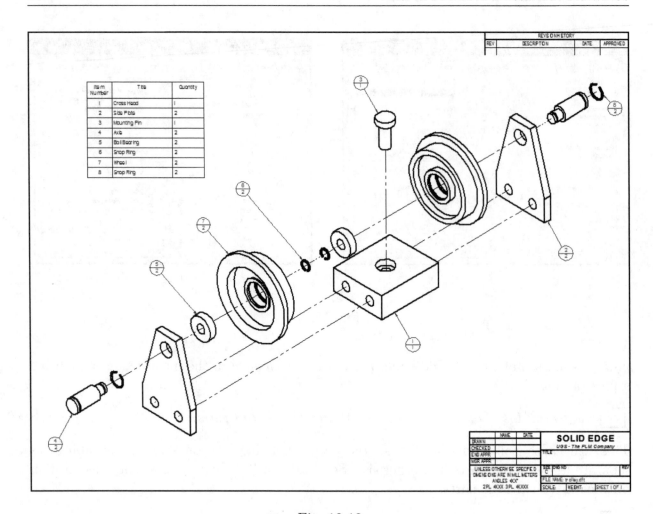

Fig. 12.12

Exercises

1. All exercises for this chapter are located at `www.pearsoned.ca/text/fleisig`. For each exercise, download the Solid Edge assembly and parts, and create a complete and correct Solid Edge assembly drawing. The drawing must conform to conventions followed in your locale.